Intelligent Sex

TRANSFORM YOUR SEX LIFE AND RELATIONSHIP

SIMON HALFORD and **NICK KEITH**

KN PUBLISHING

Intelligent Sex: Transform your sex life and relationship

First published in the UK in 2006 by
KN Publishing
PO Box 542
Forum House, Chichester
West Sussex PO19 9BZ
United Kingdom

Email: info@keithnews.com

ISBN 0 9552305 0 0

British Library Cataloguing-in-Publication Data
A catalogue record for this book is available from The British Library

Designed by Baseline Arts Ltd · Oxford
Cover by Sarah Louise Burgess
42 Mill Lane, Gosport · Hampshire · PO12 4QG
Printed and bound by RPM, 2-3 Spur Road, Chichester, PO19 8PR

Contents

DIAGRAMS

Our vision for high quality sex

Intelligent Sex promotes high and realistic aspirations for the quality of sex. Our vision is to improve your sex life and your relationships.

Sexual well-being is as important as your physical health, your state of mind, or your financial well-being, which all require an investment plan and maintenance strategy. And the way to achieve high quality sex is in direct proportion to the amount of your time and energy you invest, whatever your age.

Intelligent Sex adopts a straightforward approach to sex, without trivialising a topic which is crucially important for the vast majority of us, or without complicating the issues with medical or technical jargon.

The sexual system is subtle and intricate. *Intelligent Sex* aims to make individuals and couples aware of issues so that they can recognise and share them with their partner. Communication and collaboration will help you both to manage your sex lives effectively and rewardingly.

Intelligent Sex tackles the many myths (see the section on 'Scripts') which blight our approach to sex. For example, many people assume that a natural and spontaneous chemistry is the secret of good sex; and then later in life they accept sexual decline as normal, because they imagine that sex must lose intensity and fulfilment as time goes by.

For the vast majority of people, healthy sex means being at peace with yourself sexually, psychologically and relationally. You can enjoy sexual success with the sensible and informed approach of *Intelligent Sex*. Here is your chance to take charge of your sexual lives.

Who *Intelligent Sex* is for

Intelligent Sex is for all those
- interested in sex, and curious about it;
- seeking to improve and maintain their sex life;
- wanting to know what can go wrong so that they are prepared and can avoid problems;
- needing help with sexual problems.

Most of us suffer a decline in the quality of sex, or an impairment, at some point in a relationship, and almost certainly during our lifetime. People are interested in sex but have little real understanding or awareness of it. This is partly because they do not talk about their own sexuality and partly because the information available tends to be either too trivial, too medical or misleading.

This book tackles the true meaning of healthy sex and in everyday, accessible language deals with the questions and answers for a good sex life. We have tried to keep the technical content to a minimum by way of clarifying subtle and complex subjects, although there are a few relevant diagrams.

We want to start a dialogue about healthy sex and initiate a dynamic process of discovery. Online you will find a website at Intelligentsex.co.uk and electronic newsletters. The book will be supported by online and offline publications, a website, CDs and videos to make sex as accessible as possible in various formats. And we will also offer seminars, workshops, and more publications.

In short this book can help readers to
- develop their sexual personality
- avoid pitfalls, especially if they are starting a relationship
- get more out of sex, especially couples in a long-term partnership
- understand sexual and relational difficulties
- find answers to physical, psychological and relational questions
- gain mastery over the quality and future of their sex life.

HOW TO USE THE BOOK

The sexual models will be relevant to many, and you are invited to move about the book to discover what you want about the elements of (and barriers to) good healthy sex. However, a thorough reading of part 1 will make it easier to tackle the issues outlined in part 2.

Part 1 explores the complex realm of sexuality, and defining the nature of good, healthy sex.

Part 2 diagnoses a range of sexual problems, and advises how couples can solve them.

Part 3 features a glossary of diseases (sexually transmitted and other illnesses) which threaten your general and sexual health. Plus a resource list of places and websites where readers can go for more advice and support.

ORIGINS OF *INTELLIGENT SEX*

The book springs from the experiences of Simon Halford as a psycho-sexual therapist, in a hospital clinic and in private practice. He wanted to write a book which would deal with the everyday sex issues of everyday couples, and develop greater understanding about sexuality.

Then, as one of the facilitators of a men's group, Simon met Nick Keith, a writer and editor. He approached Nick and said that he wanted to write a book but did not know how to start. However, he knew the title, "Intelligent Sex."

Asked if this was a sexual 'how-to' book, Simon replied:

"No. It is a book about understanding and awareness. I want to describe my experiences as a team member in the psycho-sexual clinic of a National Health Service hospital in the last five years. These include case histories of people's sexual problems, real human stories and how to tackle them, usually with positive outcomes. Of course, the names, identities and some of the distinguishing features will be changed to protect confidentiality.

"People come to the clinic because their doctor has referred them to us. And, as often as not, they arrive with significant misconceptions about the nature of sex and sexuality.

"Most clients are looking for help and understanding to achieve happy, healthy and successful sex lives. And thousands more probably feel too inhibited to seek advice on the sexual challenges, which affect them every day of their lives. The point is that **sex problems are generally easy to diagnose and can be treated**.

"Too many people lose contact with their sexuality and genuine sexual needs. They shrug their shoulders, bury their natural sexual instincts, and live with unfulfilled sex lives. As often as not, such a series of events will have a serious impact on otherwise close and loving relationships.

"**To my knowledge, individual and relational sex problems remain largely outside the mainstream of our priorities**, in spite of the new-found freedom of information and accessibility for 'sex toys'. When sex goes wrong, that is a serious matter. Yet, sexual malaises and serious malfunction can often be treated and cured, restoring individuals and couples to a full and fulfilling sex life.

"My wish is to produce an informative book on sex which bridges the gap in the bookshops between academic tomes on the one side and the frivolous literature on the other. Why 'Intelligent Sex'? Well, for me intelligence means far more than brainpower: **intelligent includes elements of being smart, sensible, aware, and understanding**. And good sex is also about the physical and spiritual."

ABOUT US

Simon Halford works as a psycho-sexual therapist; as a psychotherapist, concerned with people's well-being; and as an organisational psychologist, for large corporations and public bodies.

Accredited by the British Association of Sexual and Relationship Therapy (BASRT), Simon has practised as a psycho-sexual therapist for five years. He works in a busy psychosexual clinic in a National Health Service hospital, and he also has a private practice. Currently he is researching into sexual health and maintenance.

He has practised as a psychotherapist for 10 years and is accredited by the United Kingdom Council for Psychotherapy (UKCP). As an organisational psychologist, he works as a management consultant helping with organisational and business relationships in public and private sector organisations.

Co-author **Nick Keith**, who has been closely involved as writer and editor, was Sports Editor of *The Times* where he worked for 10 years. A prolific writer and editor, he has spent the last 12 years providing publishing and editorial services for corporate customers and staff magazines.

IN CONCLUSION ...

The vision of *Intelligent Sex* is to help couples and individuals realise the full potential of sex, in terms of intimacy, closeness, expression, creativity, and intense physical and spiritual pleasure. The book operates at many levels but you will remain in charge of the choices you make. We hope you have as much fun reading *Intelligent Sex* as we have had in writing it.

Good sex is more than just having fun; quality sex builds rapport, relationships and a sense of personal empowerment. Without doubt, your greater sexual understanding, awareness, and sensibility *will* contribute to your overall mental and physical well-being.

The first person voice from now on belongs to Simon. The psycho-sexual insights and information gained from his work in the NHS and in private practice have given *Intelligent Sex* unique insider information.

Simon Halford and Nick Keith
March 2006

ACKNOWLEDGEMENTS
Jan Barringer, Ian Creber, Andrew Esson, Julie Gibbs, Philippa Hull, Geraldine Keith, Penny Power, Mairi McAinsh, Sue Malone, Professor Trevor Shelley, Terry Toms

PART I:
MANAGING YOUR SEX LIFE

CHAPTER 1

The Nature of *Intelligent Sex*

1. AIMS AND CONTENT

Intelligent Sex aims to make your sex life intelligible, manageable, and, most of all, enjoyable. I want you to feel that you can acquire mastery over the quality of your current and future sex life and relationship.

Sex is immensely important because healthy sexual activity has a powerful impact on our self-esteem, well-being and relationships. Sex is not just an issue for a few people with specific difficulties which the rest of us can ignore. We all grapple with varying degrees of problems in our relationships and our sexual world at some time in our lives.

This book will help you to find your own answers to many questions, including
- What is healthy sex?
- How do you achieve and maintain it?
- How to manage inevitable changes?
- How to manage a healthy sex life?
- How to control your sexual destiny?

For a start, people tend to trivialise sex, and give it a low priority. They talk about sex in a shallow and matter-of-fact way – the doing or not doing it – or they don't discuss it at all. People rarely discuss what works, or doesn't work. They categorise their sex life as 'good', 'bad', or 'indifferent'. They accept these descriptions as a given – taking their sexual state for granted, rather than something to work on.

Yet most people want to improve other aspects of their lives, such as career or relationships, looks or fitness, knowledge or capability. Here they look for and try to fix what is not working.

However, people tend to take a different attitude to their sex lives. They don't rate their sexuality as a fundamental contributor to their overall health, wealth and happiness.

Many derive their image of sex from the time they fall in love – a dramatic event which encourages a view of sex as being spontaneous, powerful and straightforward. Thereafter most of us spend the rest of our lives comparing our current sex lives to our first sexual experiences.

How many of us seek ways of making sex more rewarding and enriching, as we and our partnerships mature? How often do we accept the sexual onset of passive endurance in place of passionate and pleasurable fulfilment?

While you may think you may know about your sex life, ask yourself about your level of information. Test your knowledge in the questionnaires. When sex starts to go wrong or lose its lustre, you may lack the underlying framework of knowledge to enable you to fix problems and mend fences.

The beauty of truly healthy and fulfilling sex is that you can often make it even better if you are fully informed. Frankly, you are never too old to learn new tricks about sex.

Often viewed as a purely physical activity, sex is much more that this. It is profoundly psychological and relational as well as physical. These elements interact in a subtle and complex way, and we will return to them again and again. See Chapter 2.

2. THE NATURE OF SEX

Sex operates within a complex system. This will benefit from an investment of your time and effort to keep your sexual life on course, or put it back on the right track. Our knowledge of sex tends to be shallow because we have not been shown how, or taken the time, to examine its true nature. We are mostly like the teenagers who tell the older generation that they know all there is to know about everything.

When people get older they may realise that there are knowledge gaps which can be filled only by experience. As far as sex is concerned we believe blithely that (in the words of the rock band Pink Floyd) 'we don't need no education'.

Sex is the least well-known or understood of all the human activities, although our knowledge and understanding of it has improved in the last 50 years when it has become a subject for closer medical study. For example, we are only just beginning to understand the structure of the clitoris; probably no other significant part of the human body has received so little research.

Compare our knowledge of sex with what we know about nutrition. We know what we like to eat, but to stay healthy over a lifetime requires more profound knowledge. We need to be brought up to date with the research on the impact of food on the heart, on health, and on weight.

The way sex works
Sex is a highly subtle interaction of the hormonal, nervous and cardio-vascular systems. The interaction of these complex systems makes sex work effectively in humans. The mechanics seem simple but are far more complicated than erection and ejaculation for men; arousal and orgasm for women. You need to add the psychological and relational components to the sexual cocktail to the physical side of sex.

No other human activity is quite so dependent on all the pathways interacting; nervous and neurological, hormonal and sensual, personal and psychological, and relational. They are all inextricably bound up. Some parts of the psychological are partly physical, such as the way endorphins work to stimulate us. And neurological triggers for our hormonal response interact with our psychology.

As well as the physical, psychological and relational aspects of sex, we have to take account of the distinct **phases of sex**. A debate about the phases of sex was started by Kinsey in the Fifties, carried on by Masters & Johnston in their 1966 book "Human Sexual Response", and taken up by Helen Kaplan in the Seventies.

I want readers to concentrate on four phases:

Desire, Arousal, Orgasm, Resolution
- *Desire* involves attraction, interest and energy for sex.
- *Arousal* means mental and physical excitement associated with increased blood flow to the genitals in men and women.
- *Orgasm* represents the involuntary release of sexual tension, usually pleasurable, with a reflex contraction of the muscles.
- *Resolution* is a return to a normal resting state.

The issues which can affect sex are many and varied. All the sensual aspects contribute to the process - smell, touch, visual, taste, audio. In addition, you need context. Medications, such as anti-depressant drugs, also have a profound effect on sexual performance, and there are a significant number of people on such drugs.

Good sex usually requires the right context, which is often disregarded. In the early years of making love couples can overcome the context – and the more difficult the circumstances can provide an irresistible stimulus for sexual activity. Later on in the relationship these will be a barrier rather than a trigger. At other times, tiredness, privacy and self-identity have a major impact on the calibre of sex.

Because sex is spontaneous and OK when you are falling in love, you cannot assume that this will always be the case. The context needs careful management. You can't have good sex if someone or something is tickling your feet, and plenty of ticklish distractions can interfere with your sex life.

Maintaining and improving sex

Our busy modern lifestyle challenges us to achieve and maintain good sex. The belief that sex declines inevitably as you get older and your relationship endures needs to be put firmly in its place. It is a myth. Understanding sex and your own sexuality, together with an investment in time and discussion with your partner, will help couples to dispel it. The alternative? The perceived decline, or mismatch of expectations, will become self-fulfilling if couples fail to discuss, acknowledge and work on their different needs.

Your sexual activity and enjoyment can continue to improve if you are informed about the nature of your own sexuality and enjoy clear communication with your partner. There is no substitute for talking.

You are certain to experience highs and lows in your sex life. Maintaining high quality sex is a realistic and achievable goal. Most people can discover and enjoy better sex.

Identifying problems

Get your sex problem properly identified. False assumptions frequently mean that sexual problems are identified incorrectly or misunderstood. And don't rely on instinct and old wives' tales. The causes are probably counter-intuitive, so it's vital to listen to high quality systems of diagnosis rather than make assumptions.

For instance, a man with erection difficulty may convince himself that he has a physical problem; or a woman who suffers pain during intercourse may assume that the reason is purely physiological. In both cases men and women tend to resist an underlying psychological cause and reject a multi-faceted solution.

Part of the role of psycho-sexual therapists like me is to help people to understand that sex problems may involve more than one sexual domain. Men with erectile dysfunction find it difficult to appreciate the full impact of psychological causes, such as performance anxiety. Even when they do see performance anxiety for what it is, they may find it difficult to move forward and shift it.

Women may discount the advice of a consultant gynaecologist or obstetrician or psychotherapist who suggests that the pain they feel is as much in their head as in their genitals. Of course their physical pain is real and needs to be validated, but psychological factors may also contribute and be crucial to finding solutions.

The psychological components of pain have to be explained in a supportive and understanding manner, without denying what the patient feels physically. Body and emotions are constantly interacting, and this fact is even more powerful in sexual activity.

One problem with pain is that we flinch in anticipation, a psychological side effect. Women may suffer from vaginismus, a muscular spasm caused by a signal from the brain. Such a spasm can be prompted by anticipation. However, if a woman feels relaxed and in control of a situation, the spasm may be avoided or reduced. Part of the treatment for vaginismus ensures good context so that the sufferer relaxes and, if they experience a spasm, it is less pronounced.

Fixing problems

The vast majority of sexual problems are fixable, or the symptoms can be drastically reduced to start a healing process. This is clinically proven. While some problems, such as those to do with libido, are harder to treat, but all can be treated successfully to varying degrees.

Intelligent Sex aims to move people forward. Without the right level of information, you may find it difficult to get yourself in the right place for treatment. However, if problems can't be solved or improved with the help of this book, you must seek help from professional therapists through your GP.

If you have pain, check with a GP whether there is a physical reason. Interestingly, if there is pain, you may find that psychosexual therapy improves your sex life despite the underlying physical reasons. In some cases, medical treatment cannot solve the pain problem, but a therapist can help you with the psychological causes.

For example, if a man has low testosterone, part of the treatment is to give him a supplement, and that may be more effective if a psychosexual therapist supports the process. The production of testosterone is not entirely physical, and there is evidence that masturbation helps the production of testosterone. However, you are less likely to masturbate if you are depressed - so psychology can play a part in the problem and its resolution.

People have reported that physical fitness brings a substantial improvement in their sexual performance. A person who loses weight and gets fit feels better about themselves and has a boost to their sex life. Some people are uncomfortable with being overweight. And there is a distinct correlation between physical and sexual well-being.

Intelligent Sex survey

The survey has no clearly right or wrong answers, but your responses will provide clues about your attitude to sex. On page ?? you will find Simon's answers and commentary from the perspective of a psycho-sexual therapist.

Answer: True, False or Can't say

About Women

1. Women experience a genuine orgasm only through intercourse _____

2. If you can't have an orgasm, there is something wrong with you as a woman _____

3. There are different types of female orgasm _____

4. It's unfeminine to initiate sex _____

5. It's unfeminine to fantasise (or nice women aren't aroused by erotica) _____

6. It's unfeminine to become wild or unrestrained during sex _____

7. Women find it harder than men to achieve orgasm _____

8. A woman's sex life ends after menopause _____

9. It's unfeminine to masturbate _____

About Men

10. A 'real' man is always ready for sex _____

11. A 'real' man is normally aroused quickly by a woman he finds attractive _____

12. A man's orgasm is different from a woman's   _____

13. Men find it easy to have an orgasm   _____

14. Men are more interested in sex than women   _____

15. A man must initiate and take charge of sex   _____

16. If a man loses his erection during foreplay or intercourse it means something is wrong   _____

17. It's important to have an orgasm during intercourse   _____

18. Masturbation is unhealthy   _____

19. For men, sexual performance matters   _____

20. A normal erect penis is rock hard and straight up   _____

21. The size of the man's penis is important – 8 inches long on average when erect   _____

22. Men are less emotional than women   _____

Couples

23. One of the highest forms of sex is the contemporaneous orgasm, when you both 'come' at the same time   _____

24. Sex should be spontaneous   _____

25. Sex requires the man to have an erection   _____

26. The purpose of foreplay is to lead to penetrative sex   _____

27. People in good relationships don't masturbate   _____

Answers on next page

P.S. Why not take this survey before and after you have read *Intelligent Sex* to see if your answers have changed!!

Sex survey answers

In the spirit of your sexual 'master of ceremonies' I have given 'True' or 'False' or 'Can't Say' answers, although some of the issues are not so black and white. If your sexual relationship achieves top quality, you already have the answers to these questions. If not, you may want to take account of my own personal judgements, based on my experiences of dealing with hundreds of cases as a psycho-sexual therapist. Where words and phrases are underlined, seek further information elsewhere in *Intelligent Sex*.

About Women

1. FALSE. Many women never experience orgasm during intercourse. Clitoral stimulation is the most common way for women to experience regular orgasm.

2. FALSE. Many women don't have an orgasm at all, or have difficulty in having one, and yet have perfectly good sex lives. Most women can achieve orgasm with help.

3. TRUE. Some women only experience clitoral orgasm; others only vaginal; many women both.

4. FALSE. Many women carry the idea that it is unfeminine to initiate sex. Older women tend to hold that view, although I find it also in younger women. This belief can undermine the balance and quality of sex. A fair degree of reciprocity regarding initiation is preferable.

5. FALSE. Categorically so. Absence of fantasy tends to be linked with conditions such as anorgasmia and vaginismus. Women who develop fantasy and knowledge of their bodies through masturbation often experience more enjoyable sexual relationships.

6. FALSE. It is true that many women and few men share the view that 'wild' sex is unfeminine. That kind of energy and lack of restraint excites some men, although it scares others.

7. TRUE. Although some women experience orgasm very easily, it is generally true that women find orgasm harder to achieve than men, particularly during sexual intercourse; achieving orgasm often takes women longer than men.

8. FALSE. Some women say that the best sex is yet to come after the menopause. The reasons may include lack of fear of pregnancy and removal of contraception issues, and a generally more relaxed attitude.

9. FALSE. It is completely appropriate for women to masturbate. In fact it is common sense. Women who know their bodies through exploration and masturbation are far better placed to show their partner what satisfies them sexually. If a woman does not know what type of touch and stimulation turns her on and enables her to achieve an orgasm, her partner can hardly be expected to find the key.

About Men

10. FALSE. Many men have a Script that they must always be ready for sex, so they would say that the answer to this is true, but they be missing a trick. Holding this view can contribute to performance anxiety, which in turn may lead to erectile dysfunction. And if they neglect what they really want they may also develop erectile dysfunction.

11. CAN'T SAY. It is both true and false that a man is normally aroused by a woman he finds attractive. Other factors play their part in arousal – psychological and contextual. Men can become aroused by stimulation, of course, whether or not they find a woman attractive. Men can also be sexually aroused without feeling sexy.

12. TRUE. It is right that a man's orgasm differs from a woman's. There are many common denominators in terms of musculature and neuro

responses, and psychological benefits. Issues like ejaculation are distinct for men, although there is a debate over whether women can ejaculate too.

13. FALSE. Many men don't find it easy to have an orgasm. Certainly, the majority of men will struggle to have an orgasm at some point in their lives. Orgasm can become particularly difficult if a man is on anti-depressants. Some men report finding it too easy to have an orgasm (premature ejaculation).

14. FALSE. Both sexes are extremely interested in sex. It is a common mythological script that men are more interested in sex than women. Men may express their interest in sex more obviously.

15. FALSE. Many men take responsibility for initiating sex and many women collude with this. Yet shared responsibility to an agreed level (if not 50:50, then 60:40) makes for a more balanced and healthy relationship. If men always initiate they are likely to miss the powerful dynamic of feeling wanted and needed.

16. FALSE. Categorically so. Erections can go for a variety of reasons. Almost no men go through life without experiencing lost erection on occasion. The secret is to develop ways of regaining erection and don't get too worried about performance issues (See Erectile Dysfunction).

17. FALSE. While having an orgasm every time may be important for many men, learning to experience good sex in different ways makes for a more varied, interesting and creative sexual life.

18. FALSE. Masturbation is an important part of your relationship with yourself. Many men believe that they have to give up masturbating in a healthy relationship. That is their choice. Other men continue to masturbate throughout their lives. In teenage years masturbation is an important means of self-discovery.

19. TRUE. Performance does matter to men. The day men let go of seeing sex as a performance issue the less vulnerable they will become to erectile dysfunction.

20. FALSE. Men have different degrees of hardness in an erection, due to levels of arousal and how they are feeling. Many men have less hard erections later in life but still have a very good experience of sex.

21. TRUE. Men reckon that the size of the penis is important. There is a competitive element and they don't like having a smaller penis than normal. Many men come to the clinic worried about the size of their penis, but in 9 out of 10 cases the penis is normally sized. Between 6 and 10 inches is the standard size for an aroused penis. Many women report enjoying large penises, so this widespread masculine belief cannot be dismissed as a myth or script. However, in terms of pleasure most women say that the quality of the relationship holds the key.

22. FALSE. It's a common myth that men are less emotional than women. Some men have difficulty expressing their feelings, but all the evidence suggests that both sexes have equally complex emotional lives – they may show emotion in different ways.

Couples

23. FALSE. In terms of reality (although true in terms of perception). Few couples can achieve a spontaneous and contemporaneous orgasm on a regular basis.

24. FALSE. Spontaneous sex is not necessary, although people may mock a couple who have sex regularly at a particular time and place on the grounds that this represents lack of spontaneity. But if you prioritise your sex life and enjoy it at set times, you are doing better than a great many other couples. In theory, spontaneity is great, but difficult to achieve if you are out of the habit, or have busy lives, or are distracted by children.

25. FALSE. It is not true that a man needs an erection for sex, although many men and women believe this to be a fact. Men who are free of performance

worries and are happy to engage in sex without having an erection often enjoy a fuller and more rounded sex life. Women report that they find this more varied and creative.

26. FALSE. My judgement is that a healthy sexual relationship does not always lead to penetrative sex. If couples see <u>foreplay</u> as simply a device leading to penetrative sex they may cut it short and miss the rewards of a completely fulfilling sex life.

27. FALSE. Some people in good relationships masturbate, others don't. The choice is yours. In adult life there is no connection between masturbation and having relationship difficulties.

THIS CASE STUDY EMBRACES MANY ELEMENTS IN THE COMPLICATIONS OF SEX.

Tom and Polly, a vibrant and creative couple in their thirties, enjoyed a great sex life in the first three years of their relationship. They talked about everything and had similar appetites for sex. Having lived together for seven years, they decided to marry two years ago.

Polly's libido has declined over the years. This process started after the birth of their son six years ago and has accelerated recently – she has another baby on the way. They care deeply about one another and are aware that there is a problem. He doesn't want to pester her for sex, and she doesn't want to keep turning him away.

A friend of theirs has recommended that they come and see me in the clinic. Polly phoned me in advance to give me the bare details. While they are happy and life is good, broadly speaking, one blot on the horizon is that her sexual appetite is less than Tom's (see Chapter 9 for more on mismatch).

Whenever a couple come to me to restore their relationship to full sexual health and well-being, I always have a sense of excitement. I feel privileged to be entering a journey bringing a couple support and help.

When I meet Tom and Polly, my first impressions are of a radiant, dark-haired woman who is clearly pregnant and a tall. slim, relaxed and slightly dishevelled looking man. First I explain to them my working process:

"1) You tell me something about yourselves. 2) I tell you something about myself and how I work. 3) We decide whether we want to work together".

After an exchange of glances, Polly offers to relate a brief history of their relationship. 'Sex was good when we were first together, but now I don't feel like sex as often as Tom. We now find it more difficult to talk to each other about sex.'

My role is one of providing support and help.

Tom nods nervously in agreement but has nothing to add.

Then I tell the couple about my background: Having trained as a psychotherapist and specifically as a psycho-sexual therapist, I sometimes see myself as a 'psycho-sexual Poirot', who will help them find the plot, and work out the solution for themselves. And I frequently have to deal with relationship and communication issues in couples. My role is one of providing support and help.

We agree to work together and the session begins in earnest. My first line of questioning is to check personal sexual stories.

'What was sex like at the beginning of the relationship?'

'It was great and we both had similar sexual appetites,' Sally says.

'Did anything change during your first pregnancy and birth of your son?'

'Yes, massively. After the baby, sex was OK but it never got back to what it had been before. Our need for sex was different.'

'What about work?'

'Tom is in film production and I work from home as a freelance editor and proofreader. We both work hard.'

'Have there been any other important events in your physical lives?'

'It was hard work conceiving. We had our ups and downs...'

'Well,' Polly says, 'I did have an ectopic pregnancy four years ago but I felt OK about sex afterwards and it did not affect me.'

'Did you have surgery?' 'Yes, I had one of my fallopian tubes removed.'

'Anything else you can tell me?' 'No.'. Tom breaks his silence: 'Polly does seem to feel more like having sex after a glass or two of wine.'

'OK, Tom, I hear you. That is interesting, but we'll come back to that later. I want to finish dealing with the pregnancy. So, what was it like getting pregnant second time around?' I ask.

'It was hard work conceiving,' she admits. 'We had our ups and downs, and we had almost given up trying to have another baby. Finally I got pregnant when we were away on holiday.'

'What has sex been like since then?'

After Polly and Tom have explained their situation, I give my view of their sexual situation. Here is what goes through my mind as I begin my sexual diagnosis. Polly and Tom show classic symptoms in the realms of psychology, physiology, relationship and context.

As well as her loss of libido and the mismatch of their sexual needs, they have described a loss of integrity of purpose in their love-making, lack of the right context for sex, and difficulties in communication. And Polly has experienced a physiological/medical issue – her problem with the fallopian tube, which was removed after an ectopic pregnancy four years ago. Also there is an underlying threat to her fertility.

'OK,' I tell them. 'You have some issues, but they can be resolved, and here are my ideas.'

I say: 'You, Polly, have lost libido. That is clear. You both work hard, and with Polly working from home that is not necessarily good for sex. Tom comes home from work after mixing (and probably flirting with) other women in an adult world, while you Polly are at home with your young son.

'When people get home from work, they may want time with their child(ren), and anyway they do not necessarily feel sexy. Polly's surgery and problems with getting pregnant a second time have had an impact on the integrity of your sex; lack of integrity means that you have tended to have sex for reasons other than for its own sake (especially when you are trying to have a baby). Integrity is really important. So I am not surprised that you became pregnant when you were on holiday, because you were at ease and integrity was back in place.

'Tom, you have noticed that Polly's libido returns only with wine. Alcohol in moderation can be a blessing for a sleepy sex life, but it is no long-term solution to loss of libido or mismatch. We have to find other strategies for helping her to relax.'

They discussed my response and agreed that Tom believed that Polly felt that she was having sex only for the purpose of getting pregnant, and not for himself or who he was. Polly felt down when sexual activity always ended in failure. But her unconscious negative messages distorted their sexual relationship. So they had stopped having sex.

COMMENT: This case study covers a number of issues and problems which can challenge the quality of sex in any partnership. Clearly, significant events in this couple's lives have impacted on their sexual relationship and made communication difficult.

At the end of our first meeting I ask them: 'Is there anything you want to ask or add?'

They both answered with a shy smile and a shake of the head.

The treatment plan used our agreed weekly sessions (six in all) to devise strategies for increasing the wife's libido and decreasing the mismatch, while reintroducing integrity of purpose for sex. There are collateral benefits. As Polly's libido goes up, the gap in the mismatch closes, and vice versa.

How I work: People come to the clinic believing they will have their problems fixed for them by an expert. In reality I am more like a personal trainer; I work with people and support them to reach any place they want.

We work together, in collaboration, and my role is as a friend and adviser, who also has professional psycho-sexual expertise and qualifications. I have developed a set of skills to explore and balance sexual needs, hopes, fears, disappointments, and effectiveness. I help to find strategies to resolve a wide variety of sexual issues, to manage differences and unite couples in their understanding of and communication with each other. This ensures that people can rediscover and **maintain quality sex** (see chapter 3).

The couple remain in the driving seat behind the wheel, retaining control, and that has an impact on the power dynamic. If a couple has complex sexual issues, I ask them to agree a set of priorities.

Note: Mature couples with mature relationships often report that the quality of sex is as good as it has ever been, if not better. The notion that sex and sexuality decline with age or with the menopause is a myth. I meet scores of people who tell me that sex gets better with age. The frequency may diminish but the calibre improves. Sexuality functions in mature couples according to history, their relationship, their levels of communication and awareness of each other, and how they respond to age.

CHAPTER 2

Fulfilling Sex

A DEFINITION

Fulfilling sex defies simple definition or generalisation because it varies in quality and quantity from person to person and from one couple to another. Physical and emotional well-being, fitness, stress, sexual appetite and many other factors play a part.

Like all complex human endeavour, healthy sex requires constant collaboration, tuning, thought, talk and attention to detail.

While people cannot usually define fulfilling sex, they intuitively know when their sex life is good, or when it's not quite right, and certainly when it is seriously unhealthy.

WHAT IS 'QUALITY' SEX?

Quality sex means different things to different people at different times. One of the most important qualities of healthy sex is integrity of purpose. Good healthy sex has to be sex for sex's sake, just like play. If you are having sex exclusively to please your partner or to conceive, it will spoil sex.

In healthy long-term relationships good sex characteristically happens between people who talk in some depth about their wishes and dreams, likes and dislikes. It's the same story with sex. If one partner feels unsafe, healthy sex cannot happen for them.

The opposite of quality sex is what I describe as 'unhealthy' sex. This means:

1. One or more elements or phases is neglected or under-resourced by either partner.
2. Lack of integrity. e.g. Dishonesty, affairs etc.
3. Lack of integrity of purpose. i.e. not having sex for the sake of sex; it may be undermined by other agendas such as conceiving a child.

At this point I want to declare and define my interests. We assume in this book that sex is between two individuals, and in one relationship. This might not be a long-term relationship, indeed for a young couple experimenting with sex it is often typically short-term. However, generally, people who are sexually active outside their main relationship impoverish the quality of sex in a variety of ways, which we will discuss later.

While I adopt the convention of referring to opposite sex partnerships this merely reflects the majority of people who come to the clinic. However, most of the content is appropriate for same sex relationships

Although sex is not a numbers game, or a mathematical exercise, good sex can be explained in a series of rules of 3.

Good, fulfilling sex encompasses three essential elements:

- The **physical** (or physiological): these aspects of sex relate to our physical body – typically the genitals and natural sexual responses (erection, lubrication etc)
- The **psychological**: our attitudes, beliefs and feelings about sex.
- The **relational**: the impact on the relationship of the physical and psychological aspects.

If these elements are working together, broadly speaking, that will ensure 'healthy' and fulfilling sex. An example of a classic breakdown in the operation of the sexual elements might begin with the **physical** disappearance of the man's erection during penetration. The **psychological** impact is that the man thinks, "I hope that doesn't happen again – I'm not a proper man"; and the woman believes, "Maybe I don't excite him any more". The **relational** upshot leaves the man saying to himself, "I'll stay and watch TV to avoid intimacy" while his partner thinks "He can't be bother to come up to bed with me so I'm not going to make so much effort in future."

Sex also needs a positive **context** – place, time, physical well-being. Confidence and self-image affect sex.

In addition to the three components of sex you need to consider the four phases of **sexual activity**:

Desire – Arousal – Orgasm – Resolution
(People may disregard phases unknowingly)

If these aspects are broadly working together, that will ensure good sex.

As is shown in the diagram below each person has 5 areas to consider in addressing their sexual relationship.

THE ELEMENTS OF A COUPLE'S SEXUAL SYSTEM

Additionally, these five elements need to be considered within a context of place, time, physical well-being etc. And the context is the bedrock on which the various elements rest.

So, the ingredients of good sex, and a sustained and growing sexual relationship, are: Three elements working with each other in a conducive context.

Is this a big ask? Maybe. But if sex for you is only OK, your three elements and their alignment with your partner have probably slipped out of kilter.

Getting the three elements to work in harmony is achievable. Almost every couple can experience sex which is satisfying at the level of all three elements.

There are contradictions. A person may love their partner but be unable to experience healthy sex with him or her. They may find that their three elements are in harmony with another person outside the relationship – in an affair, where there are issues of trust and duplicity; or with a sex worker where health and safety are risked.

Remember the question of context. Some people may experience the most satisfying sex in the open air or in the back of a car. It depends on their personality – their need for safety and their attitude to risk and excitement. The same contexts do not appeal to everyone by any means; and they may not appeal to one of the partners. So couples need to sort out issues of context, as well as finding harmony in the three elements.

The physical element has three major aspects: hormones, circulation and neurology.

a) *Hormones*. Several varieties of hormones in an intricate balance can affect sex in a number of ways, including the drive and quality of experience.

b) *Circulation.* Physical responsiveness (e.g. getting an erection) depends on your blood pressure, circulatory system and hormonal balance. Conditions such as diabetes can have a negative impact.

c) *Neurology.* Damage to the nervous system – through illness, surgery (e.g. prostate or gynaecological), or childbirth – can affect sexual function.

Note: Medication can have profound negative affects on the physical aspects of sexual function. Most anti-depressants have a negative affect on the physical aspect of sexual effectiveness.

The psychological element also has three major aspects:

a) *Self-esteem.* Confidence and self-image affect sex.

b) *Physical health.* How do you feel? Tiredness, stress, insecurity will have an impact.

c) *Perceptions of sex.* How do you feel about sex itself?

The relational element's two major aspects are:
1. How do you feel about your partner now?
2. How do you feel about the relationship generally?

After the 3 elements of sex we arrive at the phases of **sexual activity**, which has 4 phases:
1. *Desire* – you want sex with someone.
2. *Arousal* – you become sexually excited and ready for sex.
3. *Orgasm* – however that is defined. It is debatable where sex starts.
4. *Resolution.*

Couples need to tune in to each other to achieve phase harmony. Of course a 'quickie' can be great, but most women need longer in the arousal phase than most men. (And, it must be said, there are many exceptions to that generalisation). If the man is hurried he will tend to have difficulties with his erection or ejaculation, especially when he tries to force himself from low levels of arousal to sexual activity.

DIFFERENT STROKES FOR DIFFERENT FOLKS

As I have said, the meaning of quality or good sex varies enormously between people, and for each person at different times in their life. That's fine if you can first agree about what represents quality. Sex has to meet the needs of both individuals, and for this to happen open communication is a pre-requisite.

Healthy sex normally includes the following elements:

Integrity of purpose

Good healthy sex has to be sex for sex's sake. Ulterior motives, such as achieving pregnancy or pleasing your partner rather than both of you, distort the purposes of sex. Pregnancy is a legitimate wish from sex but getting pregnant isn't sexy in its own right, if that overrides individual needs.

While couples can make healthy temporary shifts and choices to please a partner or have a baby, ultimately sex needs to be of itself or for itself.

It is also vital that both partners should want sex for its own sake rather than trying to please the other. Losing your sense of purpose will interfere with the integrity and, over a period of time, degrade the health of sex.

Rather like play, sex needs to be for its own sake, you are doing it of your own volition – willingly. You can't force people to play. It is, by definition, voluntary. Sex should be for its own sake, just like play. If you force a child to play with a toy, that is no longer 'play'. If you are having sex exclusively to please your partner or to conceive, it will spoil sex. Sex needs to be of itself and for itself. You can make healthy short-term shifts and choices – to please your partner or procreate, but if they become the norm they will cause deterioration in the quality of sex.

Successful sex is a process as much as an event, comparable with giving and receiving presents, which both require reciprocity: your giving will improve if you enjoy receiving, and vice versa.

People in their late teens or early twenties tend not to talk about what sex means to them but there is a clear understanding of what engages them. In healthy long-term relationships good sex characteristically happens between people who talk in some depth about their sexual wants and dreams, likes and dislikes. See Fantasy on page 76.

Integration of effort

Integration is about discussing, sharing and agreeing what sex is for. Compare it with going out to eat at a restaurant. You don't go into a restaurant just to feel full, but to enjoy the process and the experience of eating. As a couple, you may want different things off the menu, but you can sit at the same table and enjoy your meal – especially if the other person is enjoying what they are having.

To extend the restaurant analogy, part of the process of enjoying eating out begins with looking forward to it, expecting it. But that is not part of the meal, or is it?

It's the same story with sex. That's integration.

If one partner feels unsafe, quality sex cannot happen for them. Couples need a shared understanding of what sex is about and what they want. One partner may want passive sex and the other may want to be assertive and thrusting, and that's fine if they both agree.

Choice and freedom of choice

Sex requires a sense of freedom and choice about whether to engage or not. Choice means being able to express what you do and don't like or want – a person can say 'that's ok', or 'I like this but not that'. And it is particularly important that both partners must be able to say no, and for that to be OK.

Many people have inherited or devised their own baggage of rules and scripts, 'shoulds' and 'oughts'. Those who have no problem around sex have usually shed the shoulds and oughts, or at least have turned the volume down.

Fun, Creativity and Play

When sex ceases to be fun it becomes a challenge. If it is scary or isolating, it starts to be unhealthy. You need a sense of humour because, let's face it, there is a ludicrous side to sex much of the time. Couples who laugh and play nearly always report happy healthy sex.

Sex improves if people remember to rely on originality, novelty, and creativity. Embrace the concept of engaging in creative activity – together. It's important that both partners feel safe around creativity.

Fantasy

Encourage, explore and share your fantasies in a kind and constructive way. That does not mean you have to share all your fantasies. Treat them like dreams, as surreal indicators rather than real-life details.

Fantasy plays a major part in successful sex. So important, in fact, that we have devoted a whole chapter to fantasy in Part 3. For the time being, I urge readers to equate fantasy with dreams, and to dismiss from the mind all thoughts of silliness, smut and degradation.

A spiritual component is often the way people get close to each other and is a key indicator of intimacy. This is not exclusively so because some people have very intimate non-sexual relationships. At the same time, in good sexual relationships people tend to report spiritual intimacy.

Mutuality

Both partners get their needs met, together and separately. For example, if one partner is tired and does not feel like sex, but the other partner is eager to engage sexually, a cuddle and manual stimulation may meet both individuals' needs on that occasion. Good communication is essential to ensure mutuality within sexual activity.

Foreplay

Couples who have a healthy sex life will often engage in 'upstream' foreplay, well before they reach the bedroom. Here we mean the use of texting and messages earlier in the day or week, to provide the partner with 'early-warning' foreplay. This element is often ignored, especially in the busy lives that people lead today. Neglecting these key ingredients may lead to a loss or decline of libido and desire for sex. (See Foreplay section on page 60.)

Matching expectations

These can be expectations of each other and what healthy sex means. This tends to mean accepting of sex in a non-comparative and non-confrontational way. They accept their sexual relationship as it is, while keeping open their lines of communication. They don't compare it with what they read in the papers or their previous experiences in the relationship or prior to the relationship.

'UNHEALTHY' OR UNFULFILLING SEX
This will often have the following characteristics:

Neglect
A characteristic of 'unhealthy' sex is that one or more domains or phases is neglected or under-resourced by either partner. Then sex will be unsatisfactory and the sexual relationship may slide off on a downward spiral.

Emotional neglect – A man with stress has an erection, and engages in sex because he thinks 'That's what you do with an erection'. He is allowing the physical element to drive him when the emotional domain is not in the same place.

Physical neglect – A person might feel emotionally aroused but is not physically ready to have sex. In this case a man may not have an erection but feels aroused emotionally; he is not physically aroused, so refrains from initiating sex because he is not sure it will work.

Relational neglect – Unless there is some harmony between the three elements (physical, psychological, and relational), the sex will be unfulfilling. So, while sex can be a good way to make up if your relationship suffers a setback, this is not always the case.

Lack of integrity
A partner may indulge in sex for other reasons – such as people-pleasing (to keep or please a partner through fear or guilt or obligation). This also applies to engaging in sex to get pregnant.

Haste
Some may move too rapidly from low arousal to the sexual act. If this is repeated, it can impact on the desire phase; the desire will start to go because the overall quality of sex is impaired. Low arousal can lead to dryness or pain or an unsatisfactory experience for the female partner.

Lack of communication
Couples can go a whole lifetime with one person feeling in a state of rejection and the other misunderstood. For example, they fail to give accurate feedback on how they like to be touched.

Ignoring unmet needs
This links with communication but it also involves expressing your needs and getting them met. It is important that if you are missing something in your sexual life you find a way of expressing this to your partner.

Comparisons
With the past or with friends or with society. For example judging your current sex life against your early honeymoon period.

Mind-reading
Assumptions about what the other person is or isn't doing or thinking or wanting. It is very common, particularly for women, to assume that their partner should know what they like.

Secrets and deceit
These are usually corrosive of the quality of sex. There is a societal deceit about sex and, when people are surveyed, they tend to over- or underplay their level of sexual activity and satisfaction. Sex is like an iceberg with only a small part exposed, seen and talked about. In sex there is a huge undiscovered, unseen and unexplored area which is ripe for development. My therapeutic work is increasing the percentage which is explored and made available.

THREE SIMPLE TESTS TO CONFIRM FULFILLING SEX

1. Good communication

This is one of the most challenging aspects of a relationship. A major challenge for couples is to give constructive feedback on what is and isn't working.

Things change as couples get older or after having a baby, when women may take longer to get aroused because the arousal curve is shallower (which may be unbeknown to her). People often disregard phases unknowingly.

2. Education

Partners need to educate each other, skilfully and sensitively. Stay positive in your approach, and tell your partner what you like him/her to do; direct criticism can be off-putting. Use carrot rather than stick when discussing sex. People try something once, and their partner doesn't like it so they never try again. For example a female partner may once have refused to receive oral sex because she did not feel clean on that particular occasion.

Misunderstandings are very common, and people miss each other for years over simple issues. Sometimes it takes gentle questions and mediation in therapy sessions for couples to discover themselves and each other.

3. Updating

Another tip for high quality sex is updating. Work out what is realistic for your time of life and make peace with it. You need to bear in mind your position in the life-cycle. The cycle and frequency of sex changes as we get older; men may not get spontaneous erections as frequently as they get older.

I will deal with sexual maintenance and improvement in the next chapter.

GOOD SEX FOR WOMEN

So far I have discussed quality sex for couples. For many women, a typical characteristic of good sex is a healthy relationship with self – including their body, sexuality, fantasy, sensuality, and masturbation. Women who don't engage in self-stimulation and fantasy may find there is a negative impact on libido and the quality of relational sex. Many female sexual complaints are linked with these issues. However it is also important to note that some women report having a satisfactory sex life without engaging in fantasy or masturbation.

Upbringing

A strict or religious upbringing can stop women connecting with fantasy and with their bodies. Sexual abuse is another factor that can result in sexual dysfunction.

For many women who attend clinics there is no obvious explanation for their difficulty. Early physical development may make them self-conscious about their sexuality at school and socially. Anything that sets them apart – being tall, short, or a late developer – can affect self-confidence. Low self-esteem presents a widespread psychological problem. However, the focus in the clinic is not 'why has it happened/' rather 'how do we move on'?

Libido

Lack or loss of libido has many issues, and can be hard to treat: medical issues, such as diabetes, may cause dysfunction. The statistics on improving libido show that no single approach works better than any other. And there are no guarantees about outcomes. However, in most cases, some, if not considerable, improvement can be made. This is a journey, exploring ways for each individual. Women's libido may become low or disappear when they give birth. Men have libidinal issues about bad sexual experiences, feeling emasculated within a relationship.

Libido issues vary and people can run away from fixing them. It can be stressful for women to touch themselves. Some women need training in touching their genitals. It is less common for men to have these problems. Women clients are encouraged to do exercises at home using a self-help book.

For training through structured activities and useful books, see Chapter 14 on Resources.

If someone has been abused the physical work may be delayed. Some people are in denial, while others are aware of it. While most of the couples in the clinic have shared with their partner the story of their being abused, they have done it in a limited way. For men and women who have experienced sexual abuse as a child or as an adult, several centres provide support on emotional and other issues. See Chapter 14 for details.

Many clients who attend clinics are desperate for help, and those people are generally willing. Some recognise a problem early and go for medical help without delay, realising that it may jeopardise their relationship down the line if they don't fix it. Others suffer years of a deteriorating sexual relationship. Few relationships can withstand a seriously impoverished sex life indefinitely.

People who come to clinics in the belief that expert consultants will fix things for them will be disappointed. Others are better informed by education on TV, and recognise the complexities of sex. Some are staggeringly naive: they don't know fundamental things about their bodies or about sexual issues. Physical ignorance can be apparent in people who are otherwise sophisticated.

A couple saved sex until getting married on religious grounds. Nathan had some previous sexual experience but Ruth had none. When they attempted penetrative sex in marriage they failed and struggled for two years before coming to the clinic.

The couple came to a clinic because Ruth was suffering from vaginismus – a spasm of the muscles at the entrance to the vagina. Reassured that it was treatable – physiological work would help them resolve the problem – the couple were also given some homework of a relational and a psychological nature.

The clinical process took 6 sessions. Ruth had to discover her body at home and learn to make peace with it.

The next step was sexual activity, which meant exploration and trust. Nathan could not get carried away and start thrusting. The first stage was achieving entry of the penis into the vagina without movement. They started to relax and enjoy sex gradually.

And after six months they came back like a couple of young lovers. It was particularly rewarding work to support and facilitate. Ruth's vaginismus had been a muscular problem with a psychological component where she feared losing control. The couple put pressure on themselves to make sex work immediately.

In some cases the only symptoms of vaginismus are muscular spasms, but most people also have underlying psychological issues.

MISCONCEPTIONS: FREQUENCY MAY **NOT** MEAN GOOD SEX

Levels of frequency vary from one couple to another, and it is not true that frequent sex is an indicator of good quality sex. Undulations in pattern are perfectly normal.

Some people are compulsive about having sex but this does not necessarily contribute to quality. Many people are deluded into thinking that frequency is a good signal for the quality of their sex lives. Frequency changes: young people may be driven to have frequent sex, particularly in the early stages of a relationship.

Infrequency is hard to define. Sex should meet the needs of the couple and trying to define good sex by numbers – once a week, twice a week - is meaningless.

It is conceivable that couples can experience infrequent but extremely healthy and satisfying sex. In today's world, couples may live and work in different locations – even different continents – and meet less regularly, but still have great sex. With infrequency the quality is vulnerable if there is not good communication between the couple. It is harder to get right the important ingredients such as fantasy and foreplay, and to monitor the changes and needs of each person.

Sex should meet the needs of the couple and some couples can experience infrequent but extremely healthy and satisfying sex. Couples need a shared understanding of what sex is about and what they both want. I say again that sex will work well if people find it novel, original, and creative for them.

Health Warnings:

1. Life, experiences and people change, in sex as in other things. So don't be complacent about sex.
2. Monitor differences and changes.

CONCLUSION

The three elements and the four phases need to be balanced and well-met. This does not apply to every encounter between a couple, but overall in their sexual relationship. If any single aspect is out of kilter it will tend to unbalance the others and put a strain on a sexual relationship.

You can't share enough with your partner, or have enough information about sex.

Add in the quality of communication: a clear emotional dialogue is essential in a balanced sexual relationship.

You can't share enough with your partner, or have enough information about sex. Focus on the positive. If someone does something you don't like, offer a preferred alternative for your partner to try.

A sign of excellent communication is where the couple can have a dialogue, without one of them feeling rejected; one person can express a view and the other can say what they do and don't like about it. This is a characteristic of a healthy relationship.

Calibre and quality can get much get healthier with age. Couples who adhere to the principles of this chapter will find that sex gets better – despite the physical complications of the ageing process.

See Chapter 3.

Sex is like working out in a gym, so if you do a bit more you will get fitter. And like getting fit, sexual improvement is progressive. Even if you have good healthy sex why not explore and experiment to see if you can make it better?

Questionnaire
Sexual Health and Well being

1. Are your sexual needs being met?

Physically

a. Mostly ☐

b. Some of the time ☐

c. Never ☐

Emotionally

a. Mostly ☐

b. Some of the time ☐

c. Never ☐

2. Do you talk about your needs?

a. Freely ☐

b. Moderately ☐

c. Never ☐

3. How do you feedback your wants and needs to your partner?

a. Freely ☐

b. Moderately ☐

c. Never ☐

4. Do you talk about your preferences?

a. Freely ☐

b. Moderately ☐

c. Never ☐

5. How often do you discuss what turns your partner on?

a. Freely ☐

b. Moderately ☐

c. Never ☐

6. Can you talk to your partner about what type of touch you like?

a. Freely ☐

b. Moderately ☐

c. Never ☐

7. **Do you incorporate fantasy into your sexual relationship?**
   a. Freely ☐
   b. Moderately ☐
   c. Never ☐

8. **Do you use fantasy to increase your sexual pleasure?**
   a. Freely ☐
   b. Moderately ☐
   c. Never ☐

9. **Are you comfortable masturbating?**
   a. Very ☐
   b. Fairly ☐
   c. Never ☐

10. **Can you have orgasm or ejaculate by masturbating?**
    a. Yes ☐
    b. Sometimes ☐
    c. Never ☐

11. **Do you share your sexual inner world with your partner?**
    a. Freely ☐
    b. Moderately ☐
    c. Never ☐

12. **Do you know your partner's needs?**

    Physically
    a. Mostly ☐
    b. Moderately ☐
    c. Not at all ☐

    Emotionally
    a. Mostly ☐
    b. Moderately ☐
    c. Not at all ☐

13. **Are you satisfied with the amount of foreplay?**
    a. Usually ☐
    b. Sometimes ☐
    c. Never ☐

14. Do you initiate sex?

a. Nearly always ☐

b. Usually (70%) ☐

c. Equally (50%) ☐

d. Sometimes (30%) ☐

e. Never ☐

15. Does your partner initiate sex?

a. Nearly always ☐

b. Usually (70%) ☐

c. Equally (50%) ☐

d. Sometimes (30%) ☐

e. Never ☐

16. Do you discuss who initiates sex?

a. Freely ☐

b. Moderately ☐

c. Never ☐

17. How frequently do you have sex?

a. Daily ☐

b. Twice a week ☐

c. Once a week ☐

d. Once a fortnight ☐

e. Once a month ☐

f. Twice a year ☐

g. Never ☐

18. Is this frequency?

a. Too little ☐

b. Just right ☐

c. Slightly too much ☐

d. Slightly too little ☐

e. Excessive ☐

SCORING:

Questions 1-13 and 16: score 5 points for a, 3 points for b, 1 point for c

Question 14 and 15: score 5 points for b, c, and d. 1 point for a or e

Question 17: score 5 points for a, b, c, d. 1 point for e, f, g.

Question 18: score 5 points for b, 3 points for c and d; 1 point for a and e.

YOUR SEXUAL HEALTH PROFILE:

Analysis of Scores

75+ points: You are likely to have a healthy relationship, with high-quality sex.

50–75 points: Your sex life is probably working fairly well although there may be room for improvement in your awareness and communication.

40–50 points: Both individuals in the partnership may be experiencing disappointment, which could cause stress to your sex life and to the relationship.

22–40 points: Consider addressing some serious potential issues, possibly with external support arranged through your GP or a psycho-sexual therapist.

CHAPTER 3

Maintaining Good Sex

GENERAL PRINCIPLES

Almost every couple can achieve good sex with care, attention and the adoption of some basic ground rules (which can be adapted to meet their wants and needs). Quality and depth of experience can improve through life and into your later years.

Often couples complain, 'Sex was good at the beginning of the relationship but less so now.' Here is the inevitability factor raising its ugly head. But this does not have to be the case if people take these simple steps:

● clear communication between partners of what is working and what is not; so listen, learn and encourage each other.
● ensure you both have the appropriate level of resources;
● watch the context of sex and how it affects quality;
● regularly update each other on what is working and what isn't.

In good long-term sexual relationships, couples feel free to give and receive feedback, so that they keep up to date about each other's needs and how to meet them. They keep a clear view of the three elements, the phases of sex, and context (even if this is unconscious).

Couples with a healthy long-term sex life will tell me, 'We work hard at it; there are issues, and we deal with them. We never take sex for granted'. These people are in a minority.

Take a mature, constructive view of sexual maintenance, because what makes sex work also benefits the relationship. Sexual maintenance depends on individuals retaining their own health and fitness. Make allowances for your partner feeling tired or out of sorts sometimes, but, if a pattern develops, this may need tackling.

Honesty and integrity are the best medicine.

CASE STUDY

Patrick and Hannah are a couple in their 50s who are in the clinic suffering from a non-existent sex life. He feared erectile dysfunction and avoided any form of intimacy; she felt unwanted and was sexually frustrated, with a consequent lack of libido and a sadness that her husband was not meeting her sexual or relational needs. They had reached a point in their relationship where they felt that thay had two options:

1. to try to make a go of their marriage
2. to separate and divide up their assets.

They told me that at the start of their relationship they had enjoyed good sex. A professional man, Patrick worked hard in his business, while Hannah busied herself at home as a housewife and a dedicated mother to their two children. Sex had been put to one side, with the man feeling superfluous and the woman unloved. They had also experienced bereavement in the last two years with the death of a grandchild.

The couple had failed to prioritise sex or to communicate their needs to each other. They had simply defined themselves as a couple who were too busy to have sex; and they had not considered the impact of this on their sexual life and their relationship as a whole. An extreme example of a fairly typical problem in a sexual relationship.

Their work in the clinic involved:
a) to map the decline and cessation of their sex life and discover what had happened over the years

b) to agree a strategy for reintroducing sex into their relationship.

The strategy meant working at the three levels recommended in this chapter:
i)   communicating and openly discussing their sexual needs
ii) prioritising and having the right resources
iii) seeing how the context of their lives could be adapted to promote the first two.

And that was exactly how the couple proceeded to restore a healthy sex life. First, they talked about what they liked and disliked. The first stage of the fresh start involved being affectionate and having quality time together. Indeed sex was taken off the agenda to reduce any frustration or fear in either partner. They learned to pamper each other, go out for meals, flirt and send text messages. In a period of about six weeks they made the time and the effort to 'get to know each other' again.

They set aside one evening a week for quality time, agreed an activity which both could enjoy – a meal out, a trip to the cinema or a game of badminton – and each took turns in taking responsibility for the evening.

The next phase was to engage in sexual activity. They learned how to pleasure each other without having penetrative sex. Their sexual relationship progressed steadily, and they were restored eventually to sexual health. Hannah felt loved and appreciated and Patrick realised that he could be a more than adequate husband without penetration – by providing energy, attention and sensitivity in the relationship.

So penetrative sex became less important as an issue, whereas previously he had avoided having a relationship for fear of it failing, and Hannah's consequent feeling of not being loved had affected her libido. At the same time, their relationship flourished again. They learned to support each other as parents and grandparents, in the business and at home. In time there was also a return to full sexual activity, including penetrative sex.

In the early stages they would come to the clinic fortnightly and report on their progress. As they made progress their visits to the clinic became monthly. The process of renewal took about a year, which is a long piece of work. However they had neglected their relationship and their sex life for most of their adult lives together.

The outcome: A high quality relationship with healthy sex. This came from clear communication so that they learned to feel good about themselves and each other. They both took responsibility and felt they were in the driving seat. They abandoned any thought of parting company. A genuine success story reviving a relationship which had been allowed to wither through neglect with no ill-intent on either side.

HOW TO MAINTAIN AND IMPROVE YOUR SEX LIFE

A number of factors contribute to the maintenance and improvement of your sex life such as:

Prioritising sex

To maintain good healthy sex requires prioritisation. That is the number one priority. And you will need new priorities at different stages of your relationship.

At different times in our lives the three elements of good healthy sex – psychological, physical and relational – will change in terms of priority. Acknowledge with your partner where you both are in terms of priority, balance, and proportion at different times.

When you are young, in a new relationship or newly married, sex finds its place without much effort. Sex prospers and is a priority in its own right.

Later on, when pressure of work and family life encroach, sex may get squeezed out of a couple's busy day, or at best left to the last when both feel exhausted. This is the time for the couple to create priority time for sex.

However, people throw prioritisation out of the proverbial bedroom window. (And, of course, the bedroom is not the only place to have sex!) In a busy week you need to ring-fence quality time, not just for sex, but for closeness, intimacy and affection. The secret of maintaining a good sexual relationship is to repair and reclaim all the other bits. Put sex on the back burner while you undertake that process. Once the relationship is again on solid ground, it is easier to have a good sex life.

Couples are also fooled because their sex life picks up again when there are no time pressures. On holiday, for instance, you have loads of time, and better sex is likely to happen. When you return, make sure you keep sex on the agenda.

In business, people usually recognise the importance of managing time. Business people give clear and concise explanations of how they prioritise time for work, and how they put things right which get out of kilter. Sex is much the same, and cries out for prioritisation. Ask business managers the same question about prioritising their private life and, all of sudden, they go quiet.

It is a myth that men prioritise the physical side of sex. Both men and women are limited by this cliché: many men believe that they ought to be more physical; and in conversations with other men in stereotypical situations they may state this as their main priority. Women assume that this is what men want. In the privacy of the clinic, many men explain how they seek physical contact in order to obtain the intimacy that they miss.

Clinical experience reveals that, for many men, sex also involves:
- comfort,
- reassurance,
- closeness,
- stress reduction.

Sex is a key part of your life. It deserves dedicated time and space, concentrated energy and effort so that it can happen healthily and happily.

Put sex in the diary

Clear communication
Maintaining good sex involves talking about ideas, and sharing feelings. This will help to dispel myths and misconceptions.

Clinics record that men can be hung up on the physical side of a relationship, while women are more concerned with the relational aspect. She may not be making any physical demands on him, but he puts pressure on himself.

Many men come to clinics convinced that they must be sure of their erection before they initiate sex. Time and again the woman's response in clinical sessions is that they are not worried whether or not he has an erection. While men condemn their lack of erection as evidence of malfunction, women reveal that they have experienced the best possible sex in exactly those circumstances. This may be big news to a man after years in a relationship.

In many cases, couples only feel free to open up in front of a third party in the clinic. Then they both can laugh at their silliness. That is the whole point: sex is both special and important; it can also be silly and ridiculous. It needs to be fun.

Managing your resources
In the early stages of a relationship you need zero time, priority or resources for sex. Somehow you find time. Work shrinks to meet your needs, and you get things done, including sex. So we dress up, get ready, and find the resources in a flash – for a meal, for a drink, for a dance, for foreplay, for sex.

In a longer relationship many other factors consume our resources: children, lack of sleep, work, and tiredness. High quality sex is another demand on a couple's resources: making the most of the attention, the care, the communication and the context all burn up your energy – psychologically, physically and relationally.

The vast majority of couples try to make love late at night when their resources are low, and – surprise, surprise – find that sex under these circumstances is not so good. They choose the worst time and context to engage in one of the most important activities in their lives. No wonder their sex life diminishes and deteriorates.

As a back-up to their resources the couple can arrange for friends or relatives to look after children for an evening or a night. This will give them more room for sexual activity. By the way, the ring-fencing of high quality time may be used for affection as well as sex (or quality time). If it is specifically for sex it may feel pressurised.

As relation-ships develop, resources (or lack of them) become a highly significant issue. They are as important as prioritising sex.

Remember that sex is a process and not a one-off event. A common sexual script (see Chapter 10) is that sex is all about penetration. But, if you have not made love for some time and you are under-resourced, kissing and stroking each other will do just as well. This might lead to something else on another day.

Integrity of purpose
Sex needs integrity of purpose. You won't improve sex simply by prioritising time and your resources for sexual activity. You must honour the integrity of sex. Making sex better means having sex for its own sake.

There is nothing less sexy than believing you ought to have sex. Sometimes you fancy a bit of sex but not the whole thing. That's OK. Stick with it.

Integrity of purpose can be compromised by other agendas around sex, such as pleasing your partner, doing your duty, conceiving a child. Any of these may undermine the long-term quality and energy of sex. See also the chapter about 'Foreplay'.

Updating each other
You need to know where you are and where the other person is. Don't assume sex is the same for both partners all the time. You will experience variations in your relationship, with each other, with yourself, with your work, with your children, and with your health.

Check your physical health and your partner's. For instance, a recent cold or bout of flu will have a negative impact on your sexual well-being.

Different issues impact on both partners at different times. Be aware of this and do not allow it to undermine the quality of your relationship.

Both people in a relationship have a responsibility to keep each other up to date, and the danger of failing to update is that one party will start to make assumptions which can harm the relationship.

Self-awareness in sex

You need to be self-aware in sex, and that goes with updating. If you don't feel sexy, you lack energy or you are down, share this information with your partner appropriately.

A number of the women come to the clinic with libidinal problems and have not enjoyed sex with their partner for a couple of years or more. But they have not liked to say so. They have failed to use their self-knowledge constructively in their relationship.

Most men like to know that their partner enjoys sex, and, if not, they would probably prefer to do something else!

Suppressed information is likely to upset or annoy your partner, who feels excluded from the loop. When a professional advises a woman to confide her ambivalence or unwillingness to have sex, she often replies: 'Oh, I can't, because it would hurt his feelings'.

Being aware of changes with age – such as the impact of the menopause for women and a less spontaneous erection for men – is important.

Positive affirmation

How do you find a way to talk about what isn't working? Provide positive information. Instead of saying, 'I hate the way you touch me', or 'I don't like it so much when you touch me there', it would be better to inform your partner where, how and when you like to be touched. Or show your partner what turns you on.

There are so many ways of being positive. But some people don't seem to have this skill in their sexual repertoire, although they may be experts in the workplace. It surprises me how many people who are skilled professionally show less skill in their personal life. Successful teachers and managers get their pupils and workforce to focus on the positive and to develop dialogues, but they often fail to replicate this skill in their sexual lives.

If we don't talk and share information about a core activity like sex, it remains an underdeveloped area, at least to our partners. Some of the ways of tackling sexual difficulties involve technique. While this book is not about technique, I would say that the greatest technical skill in sex is educating your partner about what you like and don't like.

> The greatest technical skill in sex is educating your partner about what you like and don't like.

Scripts

People hold scripts [see Chapter 10 on Scripts]. For instance, a man indulging in less sex may be seen to love his partner less; if the woman always has a headache this suggests to her partner that she has lost her sex drive. People use myths to explain changes in their sexual relationship over a period of time. A common female script is: how much a man loves her is in proportion to how much he *makes love* to her.

Foreplay

People assume that foreplay becomes less important as couples get to know each other. Married people may imagine that there is no need for foreplay because they are going to meet in the bedroom, naked. Another script. Foreplay becomes more important. It can be exquisite. In a busy working day there is no substitute for a text affirming that you are looking forward to seeing them later.

A script might go like this: 'We know each other. The real business is sex. We just do it.' This is a rather simplistic approach.

And: 'When courting I need to make a pass at my partner'. [But you still need to flirt in a mature relationship. I personally held a naïve script that flirting was not necessary when a relationship was established – only in the process of getting to know each other. And I am pleased to have discovered the error of my ways!]

Activity
- *List scripts you believe in*
- *Get your partner to do the same*
- *Discuss*
- *Consider how you can each modify a script to improve your (sexual) relationship.*

Fantasy
Healthy, well-sustained sex involves fantasy, with both partners' dreams incorporated into their love-making. Unfortunately, fantasy has picked up a bad reputation – with images of bondage, whips, dressing up and behaving badly.

Fantasy is as much part of the female psyche as the male, contrary to popular belief.

Yet fantasy can excite you and turn you on. Fantasy means understanding, and agreeing appropriate ways to fulfil each other's needs. Fantasy is as much part of the female psyche as the male, contrary to popular belief.

The implications of fantasy may be more subtle than they appear at face value. Fantasy is like a dream, removed from reality. There are stereotypes about acting out extreme fantasies, which are generally unhelpful.

Avoid undermining the other person's confidence, and use fantasy positively in your relationship. See the chapter on Fantasy.

Novelty

Sex responds well to originality, newness and difference. Again, talk to your partner, get feedback on how they are with novelty or a new idea.

RECOMMENDATIONS

1. Communicate clearly

Improvement must be seen as right for both partners. If it is not right for one, fairly soon it will be wrong for both. This leads to mismatch. So one person might want sex once a week, while the other wants it twice a week.

Small mismatches in sex can become major issues over time, leading to resentment, disappointment and loneliness. Little things create big problems. Small diminutions in the quality of sex tend to be ignored.

They need to be tackled immediately. When one person experiences their partner as less amorous, that individual believes s/he is less attractive more often than not.

Many people have a secret world of trying to understand or second-guess their partner in sex. If things are not making sense, it is important to get them out in the open EARLY.

2. Talk is part of the process

Talking can be a substitute for action. While communication is vital, I am not recommending endless conversation. I recommend that talking should happen, as part of the process – and I appreciate that people resist communication. Choose the appropriate moment because to talk during sex can be unhelpful and a turn-off.

3. Take responsibility
This means giving positive guidance and direction. It is also described as 'non-blame'.

One example: A man stimulates his partner manually and she finds him clumsy and rough, so she may say, 'He's so insensitive. He hasn't got a clue.' The fact that your partner cannot read your mind does not mean he does not care.

Interestingly, when I ask the woman in the clinic how she touches herself, a typical reply sometimes is, 'I don't know. I don't do that. I haven't touched myself since I got married. It's his job.' At other times a partner doesn't take responsibility for teaching what they love, because they feel their partner ought to know.

The therapeutic recommendation for that woman is to be clear and explicit about what she wants and likes in sex. She actively shows him, and takes responsibility, rather than blaming her partner.

4. Educate your partner
Interestingly, when people have affairs they describe sex as exciting, different and new – just better. They are convinced that the new person is a great lover. But, normally, they are away from the kids and the problems of an existing relationship. And, if they leave their original partner, they usually find themselves back to where they started after a few months. Of course people are simply in the wrong relationship sometimes.

5. Accept the chance of improvement
There is no evidence that sex must deteriorate. This is a false assumption, and the reasons have been outlined above. In good sexual relationships, people assess sex in terms of calibre, not quantity.

Deterioration happens gradually. It is a slippery slope, and, when you are seeking improvement, you can slide back down again. To improve takes time and effort.

6. Treasure your resources

To improve sex also requires resources and care. Sex is an issue which is sensitive and important for both people. Sex may have deteriorated simply because one or other is under-resourced.

You may receive feedback which you don't want to hear; or give scary feedback. This can affect the pride, ego, or sexual identity of you or your partner. Valuable resources include energy, expression, time, space, knowledge and resilience.

5 Key concepts to maintain your sex life:
- Communication
- Resources
- Priority
- Context
- Blame-free honesty

Foreplay

A many-splendoured aspect of sex, foreplay is too often neglected, hurried or purely physical. Big rewards come to those who invest in the non-physical component of foreplay, beginning the process from some time (and distance) away from intimacy and building through contact to consummation (which may or may not involve penetrative sex). Foreplay deserves great attention to detail.

Many people have a limited view of foreplay, which conjures up activities just before intercourse. Male foreplay often focuses on the physical and the genitals. I would encourage men in particular to view foreplay as the best possible way of creating a good context for sex. Foreplay can include:

- Flirting
- Solving outstanding issues
- Making your partner feel special
- High quality communication
- Affection

All of these activities will serve to create a conducive climate for intimacy and good quality sex.

Over the years women have certainly taught me the subtleties of foreplay which has a variety of issues. These include thought, contact, and involvement in the ritual of foreplay. Men and women with low libido sometimes find foreplay counterproductive. But, if you don't have enjoyable preparation, sex is more likely to be unsatisfactory.

Think about the bigger picture. You can take it in turns to plan an evening or a day out, and this helps to keep the power dynamic in the (sexual) relationship in balance. This power dynamic has 4 possibilities:

1. You can be in charge and make an occasion for yourself
2. You can be in charge and make an occasion for your partner
3. Your partner can be in charge and make an occasion for herself/himself
4. Your partner can be in charge and make an occasion for you.

Alertness and thinking about your partner are key factors in foreplay.

Some people are better at worrying about their partner's needs than their own. So foreplay can help you work on underdeveloped areas. If you tend to look after your partner more, either think of how to create a good occasion for yourself, or tell your partner what you want.

It's important that couples have ways to see and acknowledge each other sexually – and flag what is missing or what works. When couples are not in the habit of foreplay, they need to develop ways of signalling sexual overtures. Try a suggestive text message, for example, and see how it is received (if it falls on stony ground, discuss and explore it with your partner).

When in work mode, men can be unreceptive to foreplay. Whereas many women go from wife to mother to lover with reasonable ease, men stay in their stereotypical boxes and think, 'Foreplay is something to do before you have sex'.

In a busy work schedule men may find it hard to take time off to tell their partner that she's attractive and they are looking forward to being closer to them later in the day. Sex becomes more of a promise, which for them is quickly fulfilled, and less of a prolonged process. I know it has been true of me: that I can become very business focused, and find it hard to switch off from work and on to my partner.

Men see foreplay as a means to an end, while women are better at playing for the sake of it. The business of play for play's sake – and caring and communicating – runs deep. You only have to see young girls caring and sharing in the playground, while boys rush around more haphazardly – of course this is a generalisation.

Many men have something to learn about foreplay, in that it is a specific and valuable activity and not merely a means to an end.

Half of the sex problems that men have would disappear if they could
   1. **learn sexual play**
   2. **rid themselves of rigid scripts that foreplay must lead to penetrative sex.**

In the clinic we may suggest that men learn to indulge in sexual play without having penetrative sex.

The process may seem functional at first, including making diary entries for written or verbal foreplay.

If you wonder about the place of spontaneity, you must ask yourself, and answer honestly, whether sex is happening spontaneously. Sex is a habit.

Sex is about energy; it's an energetic process psychologically, emotionally and physically. If you are feeling tired and under-resourced you will work less efficiently. That is not to say 'lazy' sex does not have its place in a good sexual relationship.

Good sex is also about creating space. Most people would create more space and energy for sex with their partner if they took the time to think, fantasise, visualise in the hours before they even initiate foreplay.

There's an element of the training and preparation which an athlete or musician would undergo before a performance. Athletes use visualization and concentration to a high degree before they race or play. Similar techniques are not out of place in the sexual arena.

Playing with yourself can be part of this process if arousal is sometimes difficult. If you bring yourself towards orgasm before making love with your partner, without actually having an orgasm, you may enhance the acts of foreplay and sex-play.

Becoming aroused and letting arousal subside and then getting aroused again are essential parts of the processes of foreplay. Many women find explicitly non-sexual aspects of foreplay attractive. They are turned on by dressing up to go out, having dinner together, closeness, touching, flirting, affection.

This may be valuable foreplay for women – especially those with low libido – although they may not see it as such. The non-physical aspects of foreplay by a man show the woman that he has invested time, effort and space to her emotional needs. Getting close is a long process and needs time.

Remember to maintain integrity of purpose in all your romancing and foreplay.

When the partner comes home from the cut and thrust of the office, they may possess resources from work – power, influence, variety, tension and excitement – which enable them to slip into sexual mode. However, the partner who has remained at home all day giving and nurturing may need a complete break from routine; and romantic foreplay may be required to have a sexual outcome.

Remember to maintain integrity of purpose in all your romancing and foreplay. If you go out for a meal because you want penetrative sex as the outcome, you defeat the purpose of the exercise. If you go out to communicate and get close, you are more likely to get your rewards.

Some men muddle foreplay and penetrative sex. Some of them have not learned the joys of intimacy and closeness. They get their intimacy only through thrusting bodily contact, rather than conversation, affection, hanging out together and sharing the trials, tribulations, joys and little victories of the day.

In a good interaction, the man will hear the woman's problems and listen without trying to fix them or getting frustrated because they can't find an instant solution. In reality the woman will prefer her man to acknowledge a difficulty and empathise with her – without trying to come up with an answer.

Listening sounds like a soft skill, but can be hard for men to learn. So many men come to the clinic with performance problems in equal measure to their lack of hearing properly what their partner is saying in everyday life.

See further reading.

FEMALE SEXUAL ANATOMY

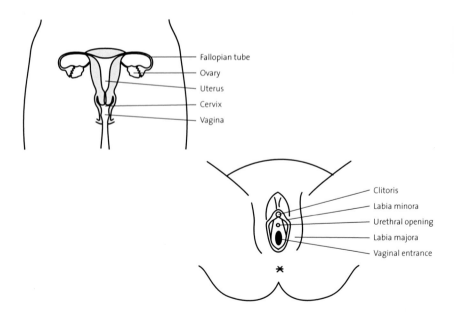

Get to know your body

Most people have a functional approach to sex. Knowing your body well is part of tapping the hidden depths of your sexuality. I would argue that accepting OK sex is settling for second best.

The way any men and women express sex and their sexuality is only the tip of the iceberg in terms of their sexuality. Developing the richer, unseen aspects of sexuality in a relationship will make sex more fulfilling and provide additional resources if the going should get tough.

The sexual history, education, experiences and understanding of men and women are different. Often women come to a clinic because they have never been orgasmic or they cannot manage sex because of vaginismus. They have problems right at the beginning of the sexual journey. For men it is the usually the opposite.

Here are some observations from my clinical experience.

WOMEN AND SEXUAL PLEASURE
For many women – those who come to the clinic and others whose sex life is not all that it might be – a key factor is that they have never found peace with their body.

Women will find plenty of useful literature to help them understand their (sexual) history and beliefs, and about being relaxed, getting to know their own bodies, and enjoying sex. Such books include *Becoming Orgasmic* by Julia R Heiman and Joseph LoPiccolo. This excellent and highly respected book talks directly to women about an integrated approach to sex, relationships, bodies, and well-being.

Many women who suffer difficulty with orgasm or never achieve one (anorgasmia) come to the clinic with their partner. When asked whether they have masturbated or enjoyed fantasy, usually they have participated only briefly and unsatisfactorily, or never at all. They don't fantasise or masturbate because they believe it is psychologically or physiologically uncomfortable.

Little girls often used to be told to point to and name parts of their body, but not their vagina, let alone their clitoris. They had to point to their ears, their nose, their hair, and celebrate their bodies, but not to what used to be called their 'private parts'. If they were seen touching themselves they were scolded and told not to do that again. Nowadays we have more sophisticated ways of dealing with this.

So these women carry scripts (see Chapter 10) about masturbation being dirty or inappropriate (whereas more men fantasise, masturbate and enjoy pornography, which has something to do with the masculine testosterone drive).

Women can be uncomfortable, and surprisingly ignorant about their anatomy.

Other women give it up in marriage or long-term partnership because they believe that they should not masturbate any longer. Some carry the script that it is the partner's responsibility to pleasure them. Although this works for some couples, it can also be an unrealistic responsibility for their partner or husband.

Women can be uncomfortable, and surprisingly ignorant about their anatomy. They don't know where their clitoris is situated, or how to touch themselves in a pleasurable way. They may have made attempts in the past and stopped because it was not pleasurable (see diagram on page 64).

In the clinic we give them books to read and exercises to learn about their bodies, to explore what sort of touch works for them. Books may be too clinical, so we tell them to go home and, in privacy, look at their bodies in the mirror and tell us what they see on their next visit to the clinic. Often their first reaction is: "Oh, I didn't like it down there."

Other sensitive issues, such as dyspareunia (deep pain) or vaginismus (muscle spasms), can be partially accounted for because they are not at peace with their bodies so they are tense when they have sex. This can get women into a vicious circle, because they believe that they ought to be able to please their partner but just feel pain and want to get sex over quickly (see Vaginismus section, Chapter 6).

The treatment is to help women to relax and nurture their bodies.

The treatment is to help women to relax and nurture their bodies with hot baths, sensuous oils and favourite music. Then they need to touch and stroke themselves to discover what they enjoy. Often they admit that they have only touched their clitoris on rare occasions, and then rather frantically. So they have pulled away from it unceremoniously.

They need to learn that vibrators and dilators can be useful. They may prefer to go to a shop with a friend or shop online. Incidentally, I advise people to buy sexual aids over the phone, rather than online because internet transactions open your email to spam. If you buy on the internet consider corresponding through an established mail-server, such as Yahoo, Gmail or Hotmail to protect yourself from spam.

If the vibrator is too intense on the clitoris, a towel placed in between may make the experience more pleasurable. People are different, so need to find their own preferred levels of touch and pressure. While some women need a great deal of stimulation and arousal to achieve orgasm, others require less. That does not mean that one type is more sexual than another. In helping women to make peace with their bodies, we have to reassure them that all sexual needs and responses are different.

They may have problems with lubrication so need to find a way of supplementing this response. There are many lubricants available. I strongly advise that you select a water-based lubricant.

If you don't know how to give yourself an orgasm, or work out what your body needs, how on earth can you expect your partner to do so?

The way a woman's body works changes during her life, if she has babies or surgery or an accident or an illness or the menopause. Women may have clitoral orgasms at one point in their lives, but later on this functionality declines and she prefers penetrative sex (or the other way around). For some women their breasts are very erogenous before their first child and less so after the birth; for others the breasts only become an erogenous zone after childbirth. They can discover this only by exploration and communication with their partners.

In early stages of a relationship, a woman's sex life may be great. Then they have the pressures and stresses of running a home and bringing up children (maybe with a job as well), so the time available to relax, celebrate their bodies and have good sex diminishes along with their libido, desire, and successful arousal and orgasm.

All too often I find that women accept this as part of their lives. I say to them: "You need to decide how important your relationship is to you and how important sex is." If the energy goes out of their sex, the relationship may well suffer. They need to consider the cost, time and potential emotional upset in having to suffer relational problems – all because they have neglected themselves, their bodies, and their sex life.

I am astonished that people allow sex to sink so low in their list of priorities that they settle for a mediocre or non-existent sex life. A typical conversation in the clinic will go as follows:

Consultant: "How's your sex life?"
Couple: "OK"

I am astonished that people allow sex to sink so low in their list of priorities that they settle for a mediocre or non-existent sex life.

"How's your relationship?"

"It's fine, fine. It's going along OK."

"Sex is ok?"

"Yeah."

"Penetrative Sex OK?"

"Yeah."

(To the man): "Ejaculation?"

The man nods.

(To the woman): "Orgasm?"

"OK."

"So, Mr and Mrs Smith, when was the last time you had sex."

"About two years ago!"

That may sound like a far-fetched scene, but it is not. I have had conversations like this dozens of times in the clinic. The point is that people tell you that everything about their relationship and their sex life is fine, because they want to believe it. People feel that it is in their interests to avoid the issue or gloss over it.

My belief is that the sexual warning light should go on for couples who are having sex fewer times than once a fortnight. Frequency isn't everything, so a week without sex means nothing, but you need to take stock if the average gap is more than two weeks.

If you aren't enjoying one of the most pleasurable human experiences more often, why not? What is wrong – not just with your sex life, but with your relationship, your sense of values and with your lifestyle priorities.

In essence, when sex is not going well for women, they often have work to do on knowledge and understanding of their body and arousal, and on learning to relax. Learning about fantasy and self-pleasure is really important for women who suffer from pain or difficulty with having an orgasm.

Recent research shows no difference between men and women in facility of arousal by sexual films, photos or stories

Some typical myths* about women and sex (held by both sexes):

● A woman should always have an orgasm – this is true for only a small percentage of women

● A sexual woman is always turned on by her partner – not necessarily if she is tired, angry, stressed, unwell

● Erotica and fantasy are inappropriate for women – recent research shows no difference between men and women in facility of arousal by sexual films, photos or stories

● Women who have fantasies are in some way immoral – many well-adjusted women fantasise about men who are not their partners or husbands. This is not a reflection on their morality. And, if they don't, that does not mean that they are frigid

● All truly sexual women enjoy exotic sex - your sexuality is not determined by whether you like unusual types of sexual activity or sex toys

● All women can have multiple orgasms – only 15-25% of women report this

● Menopause means the end for a woman's sex life – some women enjoy sex more after the menopause

● It is inappropriate for women to initiate sex – a sound sexual relationship will have an agreed balance of initiation by each partner.

* Adapted from *Becoming Orgasmic*, by Julia R Heiman and Joseph LoPiccolo

COUPLES AND SEXUAL PLEASURE

- have a bath together
- agree to have non-penetrative sex
- use start-stop method for self-stimulation
- use the stop-start method for sexual play with partner (see Erectile Dysfunction, Chapter 7)

MEN AND SEXUAL PLEASURE

"It's with my brush I make love." Pierre August Renoir (1841–1919).

When men are in their early twenties everything usually works wonderfully for them: they don't have problems with erection – generally; they have penetrative sex, ejaculate and have a very good time. Sex takes care of itself – on its own terms.

A consequence is that if sex does not go according to this common early experience men are left high and dry. Men who experience erectile dysfunction or loss of libido feel isolated because, among their mates, they will hear that everybody is always up for sex, having successful intercourse at a moment's notice. Some women say (and some men agree) of the male sex-drive: 'men are only out for one thing, penetrative sex'.

A laddish and loutish culture has come to dominate many popular radio channels, where male and female presenters daily engage in a brutish locking of horns in terms of sex and gender. Many myths are repeated and enshrined in popular banter and in the words of pop songs.

What happens to men long term? They often know all too little about their arousal, fantasy and relationships systems. So they are discomforted by their own anxiety around performance and responses to stress because they have not learned, understood or developed a realistic relationship with their own body.

Further down the line in an established relationship, all their assumptions about immediate arousal and ejaculation on demand are challenged. They have little resource in, say, their forties on how to manage or counteract sexual problems.

Myths and misconceptions are instilled deeply into men from their fathers, brothers and peers, so they have little idea about what to do when sex ceases to work. If an erection is lost it can be devastating and the beginning of a steep and quick downward spiral because they don't know what to do or where to go.

If they are having difficulties with performance or sexual drive they should make an appointment with a GP and ask for a referral or for a name so that they can make arrangements privately. Check that the therapist is accredited with the BASRT. Things are best nipped in the bud, so avoid falling into the trap of thinking 'It's not too bad'.

Are there positive things for men to do? Men will find solace if they can look at sex in an integrated fashion.

There is a lot for men to learn on this level. For example, they need to make themselves aware of attitudes and views absorbed about sex, marriage, masturbation and childbirth from their parents; they need to get to know their own bodies, understanding touch in first a non-sensual way and then sensual. From that they will learn the nature of arousal in terms of touches. Then they can develop fantasies which integrate the mental and physical worlds.

This provides a rich swathe of information about themselves to transfer into a relationship. There are a number of phases in getting to know your sexual response and responsiveness, and lots of practical exercises designed for women which can be used by men.

If this all sounds rather difficult, perhaps un-masculine, I have to tell you that men come to sex clinics only when something has gone wrong. However, it is also true that you think your sex life is OK because everything is working well. With more knowledge about yourself, your history and your sensual patterns, you can give yourself and your partner more pleasure.

Many men are embarrassed about the acceptability of their genitals - to women, to other men in the changing room and to themselves. The old cliché that size matters is constantly reinforced – even in car advertisements. Men can become concerned about how they manage sex, not just performance anxiety but about giving their partner satisfaction. Hormones and youth keep these worries below the surface enabling men to perform until other factors encroach.

Many men don't know what is stimulating and pleas- urable when they are inside a woman.

Stages of arousal

If you ask most men, "How do you know you are aroused?" Most would say, "Because I have an erection". But that is nonsense. Several things need to happen prior to an erection before it qualifies as true arousal. Erection can easily happen without arousal, so men engage in sex thinking they are aroused when they are not. Their partner may think their man is up for it and so acquiesce. In short one can be aroused without an erection, or not aroused with an erection.

So the couple are ignoring the physiological, emotional and psychological aspect of the sexual equation. Men are reducing themselves to a machine that has an erection or doesn't, and think that is what sex is about.

Many men don't know what is stimulating and pleasurable when they are inside a woman. For example, by far the most sensitive area of the penis is the frenulum, a skin tag on the undersurface between the glands and the shaft. However, men often don't know exactly where their pleasure comes from and what does and doesn't work for them.

Many men don't understand their bodies so they are not aware that the whole body can be aroused. The focus is reduced to the single aim of getting an erection for penetrative sex. Here they are relying heavily on a number of things happening, and so it's a dangerous route. Yet many of the men I speak to in the clinic are on that course.

It's like footballer Michael Owen saying 'Give me the ball in front of goal and I'll score'. And he often does. However, if he were to fail with a series of penalties, that might cause a loss of confidence and a dip in his general goal-scoring performance.

For men, there is a high focus on their sexual performance and so they put high pressure on themselves to score. If a footballer starts to fail with his penalty kicks, he, the team or the manager may decide to 'rest' him from the responsibility of taking penalties for a while. In sex, men 'go for goal', lose an erection, fail with penetrative sex, and feel more pressure the next time they are going for goal – which merely exacerbates their problem with having an erection.

The sexual solution removes the performance pressure, which includes trying more foreplay (see Chapter on Foreplay) and other sexual activities (see the Chapter on Erectile Dysfunction). The expectation is that they will rebuild their confidence by having different sexual successes.

Enhancing male pleasure

"If it's working, why change it," is a common and not unreasonable attitude. But it depends on which levels of your sex life are working. If a man is achieving erection, penetration, and enjoyable sex, let's look at ways that he can enhance that. Whatever is good can become better and eventually best.

Straightforward sex is good, but it may become boring and enjoyment may not go on forever for both parties in the relationship. When sex works well, it may be that couples have spent a little time thinking about arousal and about their bodies – what works best.

There are benefits in each partner exploring his or her own body to find what works best, and perhaps moving away from the penis. The idea of 'erogenous zones' is essentially male and essentially sexual. But relaxation, calmness and physical comfort and safety are interesting states for men to work on. Otherwise there are dangers that sex will become stressful, and related to anxieties. Creativity, play and fun may get lost.

It may surprise men to discover that a flaccid penis is a sensual part of the male body. Remember a limp willy still 'counts'. After all, none of the great works of art are painted with men displaying a massive erection, but the pictures are still sensual.

Sex works best if it is a process, starting with a period of relaxation and enjoying being with your partner. Men had better get used to this because 50% of them will experience erectile dysfunction at some time in their lives. Sex is not an isolated incident.

Men want to fix things, as I have said – which is a typical pattern. Sometimes they must sit and listen passively, to understand their partner's wishes and needs.

COMMENT
It's so important for couples to communicate about bodies and their physical preferences. On many occasions couples return to see us in the clinic with the good news that their sex life is improving, simply because they are talking to each other about their likes and dislikes.

MALE SEXUAL ANATOMY

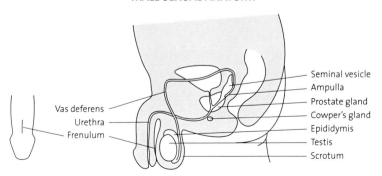

Vas deferens
Urethra
Frenulum

Seminal vesicle
Ampulla
Prostate gland
Cowper's gland
Epididymis
Testis
Scrotum

Fantasy

Fantasy is a much-misunderstood part of our sexual lives and our sexuality. It is deeply rooted in our nature. People subdue, suppress, avoid, and deny fantasy rather than embracing it and cultivating it as a positive part of their sexual lives. The challenge is to integrate your fantasies into your sex life.

Human beings think about sex several times an hour and yet all too few of us are satisfied with our sex lives. We keep a large part of our sexual dreams, wishes and desires below the surface, and never quite manage to tap into them. Here is where fantasy can play an important part in finding fulfilment.

Often dismissed as unsavoury, inappropriate, or unmanageable, fantasy opens up a new range of intimacy, creativity and novelty. Couples who delve into their fantasies constructively can find new ways to meet their deeper or hidden needs in a relationship.

Making peace with your fantasies, and developing and weaving them into your sex lives, can give you an invaluable resource. Many people feel uncomfortable about fantasy, both men and women, but often for different reasons. However, avoiding fantasy often correlates with poor sexual function and with psychological and physical problems, such as low libido, vaginismus, erectile dysfunction and so on.

Men may be surprised to discover that their fantasies mirror those of women. Interestingly, clinical work confirms that many women have similar fantasies to men. There's no greater bond for men and women than to share their fantasies with each other, if the process goes well. (To discover what can happen when the process goes wrong, see the Case study: *Voyeurism*, in this chapter).

Much fantasy, for both men and women, can disturb them if they interpret it literally. Fantasy is like dream: it's symbolic, complex, and surreal. There is a world of difference between using fantasy in an inclusive way rather than acting it out literally.

For example, some men and women fantasise about violence, power and submission, and, given issues of rape and the political correctness of modern society, such fantasies may disconcert them. One way for men and women to manage this may be to talk to each other, and confide in 'safe' friends, about the nature of their fantasies.

People have a vast reservoir of sexuality within them but often connect at only one small level. Sex meets all kinds of subtle and complex needs, but many of these are often untapped. So fantasy provides a productive area for exploration.

How do couples open up fantasy for each other?

The first issue is to agree a set of ground rules. Some people have deeply embedded views about truth and reality, which makes this difficult. Remember that fantasy is surreal so you need to manage how you share your sexual dreams with your partner. So many people feel isolated or hurt by their partner's fantasies because they are presented and/or heard literally.

It is important to distinguish between fantasy and reality. Many women feel that fantasy is wrong because it shows disloyalty to their partner, especially if they view sex as about pro-creation and not about self. You need to think about the deeper messages in fantasy and weave them into your relationships.

CASE STUDY: GROUND RULES

Ken fancies his neighbour Marilyn because she takes pride in her appearance, looks slim and fit, and smiles at him engagingly, while his partner Karen has put on weight, doesn't appear to care about her looks any more, and has lost her edge. Ken's fantasy is that he likes a good dresser with a toned body.

It is destructive for Ken to tell Karen, "I fancy our next door neighbour Marilyn, why can't you be more like her?" He might say, "I realise we have both put on a few pounds so why don't we go to the gym, take some exercise and lose a bit of weight?" This informs their relationship in a constructive way and takes it forward.

COMMENT
Find a positive and creative way of letting your partner know that you enjoy their body more when s/he is slim and/or dresses smartly. But you need to manage this sensitively and without criticism.

Ground rules:
1. Don't compare your partner with others
2. Don't suggest a fantasy in such a literal way as to reveal that you fancy someone else.

POWER AND DOMINATION
Several men and women come to the clinic worried about their arousal in rape or violence fantasies. If you dream or fantasise about rape* (see box), talk to your partner about issues of domination, power and powerlessness.

Most men have fantasies about rape at some level, or being taken/raped; and a surprisingly high number of women also fantasise about rape. Such fantasies revolve around power dynamics. They can be explored in gentle games and you don't need elaborate bondage.

There can be a fine line between excitement and fear, even a relationship between the two (like many other human polarities, such as love and hate).

Being highly aroused through fear is not physiologically very different from arousal by sexual excitement. The body cannot necessarily differentiate between the two types of arousal, although they are not the same thing.

RAPE FANTASIES

Women who have been raped may continue to be concerned about the non-consensual sexual experience. They express great concern at their sexual arousal during the attack – and they may even have experienced orgasm.

While the physical rape incident may have been dealt with at the time, the victim's internal psychological issues may remain hidden and re-surface at a later date. If the woman has previously experienced fantasies around rape, she will fear that she secretly wanted it or colluded with the rapist. We remind her that

- Fantasy is normal
- She did not seek or deserve to be raped
- Sexual arousal is a physiological response to stimulation, which is not within your control, and it is distinct from psychological desire.

HELPING TO DEVELOP FANTASY

This is a subtle issue for couples, with several stages.

1. Find your preferred medium for fantasy – i.e. what is likely to work.
What types and methods of sexual dreams work. Literature with romantic and sexual ideas works for many people, especially women. Others prefer a visual or auditory stimulus – watching a video or listening to a tape. Most of us have preferences: men tend to be visual, and women literary, but this is a broad generalisation.

Today women can be visual, which they would have denied themselves 30 or so years ago. Women today find it more acceptable to be visual.

Visual eroticism comes in many forms: there are sexually explicit films on the one hand or, on the other, Michelle Pfeiffer doing her piano number in 'The Fabulous Baker Boys' – and even more subtle sexual comedies and dramas (often French or Italian films). Settings, suggestions, inferences, conversations and silences can be as sexually stimulating for some people as explicit sex is for others.

2. Discover the barriers and limiting factors.
Remember that fantasy which works for you may put your partner off. So you need to find palatable forms of fantasy which work for both individuals. Some people reckon that fantasy is being unfaithful to their partner. Yet most men and women fantasise about others during sex, enjoying imaginary sexual 'adultery' at some time.

Women often tell me in the clinic that, for them, fantasy is naughty, dirty and inappropriate; these women would disgust themselves if they had thoughts and fantasies about, say, a strapping, bare-chested young man who they see working out of doors.

In the Victorian era, respectable literature cultivated male and female fantasy. This was an age of repression which was thinly disguised in literature. Even Jane

Austen has undertones of sexuality, and when this is brought to the screen... people still talk about the sexual power of the recent BBC TV adaptation of 'Pride and Prejudice', especially the scene where Darcy (Colin Firth) dives into a lake and swims across, emerging with his wet clothes clinging to his body.

The key question to ask is: 'What works?' The above scene touches on some notions of masculinity and being natural. Aspects of that fantasy can be taken into a relationship without the drama of Darcy.

Fantasy is like a dream. Interpret it creatively and use it to provide a valuable resource to enrich your relationship.

3. Allay the fears.
Fantasy can scare people. They are scared, about their partner's response, about their own sexuality, about what it all means. What may seem inappropriate to you is exactly what turns your partner on. You have empathised with other people's set of values and suspend your own beliefs, myths and preconceptions. Indeed your partner's dreams can help you rediscover parts of your personality which you have suppressed or denied.

The answer is to listen and also express your own sexual feelings and desires.

People shy away from fantasies because of what they mean to them rather than what their partner gets out of it. The modern man who says he is too 'caring and sharing' to play power and bondage games in the bedroom because they are 'inappropriate' may be surprised and released when he gives himself permission to get down to it.

Fantasy throws up needs which are not being met. For 90% of people in long-term relationships, malaise may start when fantasy stops or is not fully explored. If you ignore the needs of sexuality, personality, intimacy and emotion you may risk undermining a long-term relationship. When you find them, all of a sudden you will enjoy a richer and deeper relationship. Many long-term relationships come to grief because the couple deny their dreams.

This comes through in the clinic. When you talk to people who have deeply satisfying sex, the characteristics of their sex lives usually include fantasy, communicating and conversation, flirting, fun and foreplay which are both sexual and non-sexual. We hear this again and again from couples who come to us for help because a good sexual relationship has been knocked sideways by an illness or accident, and the couple want to re-discover it.

CASE STUDY: GENTLE FANTASY

Laura, an attractive, fine-boned redhead in her mid-40s, came to the clinic suffering from anorgasmia. She did not want to raise it with her husband Doug, let alone expect him to come to the clinic.

When I asked her whether she felt comfortable with her body she shrugged her shoulders, uncomfortably. So I asked her if she masturbated, and she frowned and shook her head.

"Never?" I asked.
"Never," Laura replied, rather indignantly.
"Do you have fantasies?"
"No."
"Have you ever enjoyed anything to do with erotica?"
"I don't engage in that sort of thing at all."

I discovered that her upbringing was prim, and her parents had Victorian values. She had been sent to a single-sex private school; so the subject of sex was never discussed at home or at school.

At an intellectual level Laura understood the notions of foreplay and fantasy but she had never once explored her own sexuality. At first Doug had pressed her for sex, but had lost interest over time because his wife was not getting any pleasure out of it. [His attitude to sex was somewhat brusque and his sexual subtlety mirrored the character in *Mrs Doubtfire* who reported that her husband approached foreplay with the words, 'Brace yourself, Effie'.]

Laura was worried that their relationship was at risk – that her husband might stray because of an unsatisfactory sex life. She told me she wanted to tackle her difficulties with orgasm, felt confident in taking my advice, and expected me to be straight with her. So I asked her:

"Tell me, Laura, if you are not at ease with your own body and don't know what turns you on sexually, how do you expect Doug to know?"

The process started with getting her to take time exploring her body

The process started with getting her to take time exploring her body at home, and the first two steps were: 1) to examine herself closely in the mirror and then report back to the clinic exactly what she saw; 2) to consider what turned her on sexually.

Laura went away with a heavy heart, unsure about the 'homework' she had to do. When she returned for a second session she reported that the process had been extremely uncomfortable. While she thought her body had the right proportions, she did not want to think about her anatomy or her genitals.

I encouraged her to get to know her body gradually, taking a long bath and learning to pleasure herself gently. This took several sessions, but eventually Laura reported that this 'education' process was beginning to make sense to her. She was able to say what types and pressures of stroking she enjoyed. This was an extremely gradual process, but slowly – involving fortnightly discussions at the clinic over six months – Laura formed a better relationship with her body.

As for sexual imagery, she was put off by anything which was too graphic, but found that soft images and subtle suggestiveness aroused her. The imagery included sensitivity, affection and touch.

And Laura also fed this information into her relationship with Doug. After six months she was able to masturbate and achieve orgasm, and enjoy sex more, especially if they were on holiday or their teenage son and daughter were away with friends. So context was extremely important for her, as it is for most of us.

She felt more at ease about telling Doug what she wanted and what worked for her sexually. Gradually, her libido increased and their sex life improved. She left the clinic with a reminder that her sexual life (and their sexual success) needed constant prioritisation, a good context and sensitivity in fantasy, foreplay and having sex itself.

Troubling fantasies

Fantasies and dreams can trouble people. A young man came to the clinic distressed that he fantasised about hurting women and being aroused by inflicting sexual erotic pain. He was worried by the fantasies which had obsessive/compulsive elements. He would search the internet to live out these fantasies and became hooked on the process.

However, he was mindful of the implications for his relationship with his partner. In their relationship he was sensitive, caring and met her needs. When I suggested that he might try getting some part of these fantasies met, he was horrified, because he believed his partner would hate the idea.

So I recommended that he discuss with her issues of power, dominance and exploring incorporating small degrees of pain in their sex. His partner said immediately that this was a great idea and had experienced her own fantasies around giving and receiving pain.

Before long they explored gentle bondage and use of blindfolds, playing with taking it in turns to be submissive or dominant. He found a decline in his obsessive / compulsive behaviour in which he sought satisfaction in violent sex through the internet. He found that his negative self-perceptions were being met safely in the relationship resulting in increased confidence and sense of self-worth.

Sometimes in the clinic he was moved to tears in describing how his powerful fantasies were included and contained; that they were accepted and had become part of the relationship. He was given permission to own his fantasies and not be ashamed of them. He reported that intimacy and pleasure increased for both of them.

Of course, this scenario will not work for all couples, but it shows the importance of communication, discussion, exploration and sharing responsibility. You have to be careful because sometimes this can go wrong.

COMMENT
The ways of exploring troubling fantasies include:
- Being lateral, not literal, in your interpretation of fantasy.
- Not comparing your partner with other people.
- Ensuring safety, e.g. having signals or passwords so you know when to stop.
- Sharing your wishes in an exciting and informative way with your partner.
- Making suggestions and exploring possibilities
- Being sensitive to each other's sexual tastes.

CASE STUDY: VOYEURISM

Fantasies involving voyeurism occur in both men and women. While they are more common for men, we do find them in women, and here is a case where sharing and acting out a voyeuristic fantasy has gone badly wrong.

Rachel had an overpowering fantasy that she wanted to watch her husband Richard have sex with another woman. Their sex life was already satisfactory and Richard resisted for a long time. But Rachel persisted and eventually Richard agreed.

When the fantasy was brought to life and Rachel had seen Richard making love to another woman, she was horrified. Richard, who had expected to be uncomfortable and dissatisfied with the experience because he loved Rachel, found that he enjoyed it and wanted to do it again.

He assured Rachel that he still loved her and reminded her that this was her fantasy in the first place. But Rachel put her foot down and said that she never wanted it to happen again.

Their sex life resumed its familiar pattern, but Rachel became increasingly suspicious and jealous. She resorted to having her partner followed, and soon discovered that he was indulging in occasional but regular secret meetings with different women. When she challenged him, he admitted that he had developed a penchant for sex with strangers, but he still loved her and wanted to work it out.

Sadly, the couple tried and failed to find a way of accommodating and including Richard's new-found fantasy. The result was separation and divorce.

COMMENT

While communication in a relationship is almost always healthy, the resulting change can be risky if both individuals cannot agree, or fall out over the path to realising and including the fantasy in the practice of the relationship. Acting out some aspects of fantasy, especially in extra-marital relationships, is usually destructive.

'FANTASTIC' WAYS FORWARD

1. Find out what works.

2. Discover barriers. What makes you or your partner anxious about sharing fantasy? Is it fear, embarrassment, a sense of inappropriateness? Find out the boundaries which limit the exploration of fantasy.

3. Explore together generally. Buy a video but watch it with an open mind (not a critic's eye to quality). Have fun. Flag up to one another things that do and don't work for you. Remember to think and talk about your reactions to what you see and hear. Avoid concerning yourself with the quality of film-making, plot and dialogue. Too often, couples who come to the clinic with libido problems and are sent home with instructions to watch a sex education video, come back to us with a catalogue of criticisms about the storyline. Imagine yourself in a dream rather than watching real life.

Once you can tell your partner what is exciting, what's less exciting and what is off-putting, it becomes much easier to share your fantasies. You may well find that explicit sex on video turns you off. So try different kinds of videos, books, tapes and CDs.

This will help you have a dialogue about what sort of sexual person lies below the surface. **All too often, people with unfulfilled or unhealthy sex lives do NOT explore or develop their fantasies**, whereas couples with a happy sex life usually do.

4. Resources

As well as videos and books, the internet offers an abundance of resources for fantasy. All you have to do is type in an erotic word into a search engine. Some words of warning: when you enter sex websites you may be opening your email box to spam.

COMMENT

If a couple have a wonderful sex life, and both are happy, they may not need fantasy. If not, they may be missing a trick, because they are not being three-dimensional around sex. My advice is to share and explore your fantasies.

Relationships and sexual togetherness have their ups and downs. Sharing and exploring fantasies is usually a good way to sustain and improve a healthy relationship and a quality sex life.

PART II:
SOLVING PROBLEMS

CHAPTER 4

The power of relationships

Relationships are paramount in sexual relations. Relational problems often underlie the sexual difficulties that couples present at the clinic. In this sense particular attention must be paid to the relational part of the three elements (psychological, physical, and relational, as mentioned in Chapter 2). Even when dealing with the other elements, a high priority for one or both of the individuals is the relationship.

When sex between partners becomes troubled or less satisfactory, this will almost certainly impair the character and quality of the relationship as a whole. Equally difficulties in the relationship are likely to affect the sex, so somewhere in the cycle there are relationship issues, in the background or foreground, which need investigation.

It is simplistic to say that 'there is a relationship problem', because it is not necessarily a problem in the relationship causing a sexual issue; but the sexual issue will have an impact on parts of the relationship. To treat a person as a whole they need to look at relationship problems which may be a cause of, or generated by, other issues.

People tend to resist a relational diagnosis. If one individual has a physical problem, the other (or both parties) might look for a cure, by way of a pill or some other medical interaction. Generally couples are loath to hear that they need to do something about their relationship as well. They would prefer a quick fix, a pill or a tablet.

Viagra compounds this issue because it works in the short term. Viagra doesn't fix the problem, it masks it, and you don't want to have to take a pill for the rest of your life unless it is essential for medical reasons. Some consultants will not prescribe Viagra unless the couple are willing to examine other issues in the relationship as well as the physical.

Women seeking to end pain may have picked up an inference from the medical profession, either subtle or unsubtle, that the problem is all in their mind. They find it validating when the consultant confirms they have a physical issue, and acknowledges that their pain is real. However, when the consultant goes on to suggest that there may be relationship issues, a woman may go back on the defensive, saying: 'Ah, it is in my mind then'. Pain can be both real and psychological.

Complexity of sex in relationships
The key point is that sex is one of the more complex aspects of a relationship and it impacts deeply on each individual and the couple. Many people 'take sex for granted' – a physical given, and they confuse the psychological and relational issues. People tend to mix 'issues' with 'problems'. There is a difference in this context.

In sex, couples interact with each other in the closest way imaginable. When something happens to change that interaction – a new baby, or erectile dysfunction or vaginismus, or stress at work, or losing your job or the death of a friend or relationship – that has a deep effect on the individuals and the relationship.

a) Pain is poorly understood
A woman comes to the clinic suffering from painful intercourse; you have reassured her that the pain is legitimate. We explain, when talking about possible psychological issues, that the client might not be sufficiently aroused for penetration, for example. As women do not have to 'perform', they may put up with a foreshortened period of foreplay and they go along with the pace that their partner dictates. Often we find that sex is pain-free or arousal works well when they are relaxed – on holiday, away for the weekend, without their children.

The question then is: how does a couple accommodate different rates of arousal? There are lots of ways of achieving this and having fun. One person's pain, or lack of arousal, remains valid and true. But the couple can take steps to

CLOSENESS AND SEPARATENESS OF RELATIONSHIP

Which best describes your relationship in terms of closeness? Any are fine if that works for you. I find in the clinic that 1 doesn't work for at least one of the couples and they feel isolated or lonely, and the relationship may be vulnerable to drifting apart. Equally, 4 can leave one or other partner feeling overwhelmed or claustrophobic.

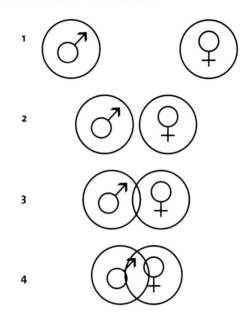

avoid that in the relational process. This is a communication issue for both parties; and men need not feel that they have been insensitive or a 'bad lover'.

So, resist taking responsibility or blaming the other. Few people can read another person's mind; unless their partner lets them know what is going on, it is impossible to get it right. This is a clear example of how good communication about issues within a relationship can solve a real physical problem. Both partners need to communicate their personal issues.

Pain during intercourse is poorly understood and, if people can't find a physical cause, they are often quick to associate it with psychological causes. That is what we hear in the clinic from clients who have been referred to us. There are various causes of pain: some of them are mainly physiological; most of them are a complex interaction of the three elements. Pain has various components.

b) The Value of Maintenance

It is often assumed that sex is a simple thing which runs on its own. It isn't. Think of buying a brand new car, and the excitement you have when you drive around in it. That's like the beginning of a relationship. But you need to maintain and look after your car over the years. Imagine your car has gone three or four years, and has 30,000 or 40,000 miles on the clock, but you have not serviced it or changed the oil. What would happen? Sooner or later the car will break down and fail.

Relationships and sexual relationships are infinitely more sensitive and complicated than a car. However, people have a naive view about sex. This is understandable, because at 19 sex is simple. Certainly, for most young men, sex takes care of itself: arousal is no problem; and libido tends to be high. In most cases, sex goes swimmingly for the young. By and large, as the human bodywork and internal mechanics age, combined with additional life pressures, more issues show up on the maintenance list.

c) Significance of Trust

Trust is another big issue in relationships. Many men assume they are good lovers if their partner makes some noise during sex. Some women fake orgasm, which is very confusing for a man, even if she does it in the interests of pleasing him. Men are left wondering what the baseline is. Few men fake ejaculation – unless they have a particular issue like delayed ejaculation – but it is more common among women. Perhaps this is because the woman has bought into a script and feels that 'she needs to protect her partner's fragile ego'.

Men are often distressed to hear that their partner has been faking orgasm because it undermines trust. This behaviour is self-defeating and puzzling. Remember that couples can have a great time having sex without orgasm. A man who is having difficulty with orgasm will benefit if he can talk about it to his partner. Isolation and secrecy can be very destructive for the individual and their partner.

RELATIONAL ISSUES HAVE THE FOLLOWING KEY ASPECTS:

1) Communication and problem solving

A couple may talk to each other without saying what works best for them in sex: how and where they like to be touched; the preferred degree of pressure, whether they prefer stroking or rotation. Usually couples will fudge it in conversations. Few couples who discuss problems in detail, and those that don't will experience a deterioration in their sexual relationship.

In consultations, people may first resist having such intimate conversations, on the grounds that they remove romance. Yet there are times when you need to talk intimately and these very conversations will protect their romance. If you explain what does and doesn't turn you on, you will be much more romantically inclined when your partner tries to fulfil your stated wishes. They too will feel more romantic when they can articulate it, work on it, and get it right.

Poor communication can damage a relationship. Conversations between couples can tease out misunderstanding and muddle. For instance, there may be a difference for each individual between affection and sex. Some couples need to take sex off the agenda – to re-learn how to be affectionate with each other without having sex; they may have been avoiding affection because it leads to sex.

2) Affection

Removing affection from the relationship can leave you high and dry. With no sex and no affection a relationship will be stranded on sterile ground. It will only be a matter of time before one of the parties becomes disillusioned and seeks a new source for affection and sex.

More effective communication helps. And taking sex off the agenda for a while can restore the couple to a more sophisticated relationship, allowing their sexual life to recover and blossom again. This process is liberating.

3) Time and Prioritisation

Failure to prioritise and devote time is another issue. Life pressures from work or children may get in the way of individuals or couples giving priority to their relationship.

4) The modern work-life imbalance

The modern generation has a different set of issues. Young men who don't perform the first time may not be ready for sex, but they immediately find themselves trapped in a vicious circle. Sadly, non-performance can lead to depression and even suicide.

5) Scripts within relationships

Scripts can get in the way and prevent couples in a longer term relationship from continuing with foreplay and wooing. In the busy world of work and children, couples stop touching, kissing and cuddling; keeping a space for themselves where they can say that they find each other attractive.

6) Planning the context

A couple may try to have sex late at night, when the children are in bed and when one or both are tired. Sustaining the energy and context to enjoy a high quality sexual relationship requires logistical planning. Not to do so may leave one of them vulnerable to a new relationship outside which does not carry any of the baggage of their existing partnership.

So...

- allow your partner to know s/he is important
- show your partner that you prioritise their needs
- tell your partner the relationship is ring-fenced.
- take responsibility in turns for providing time (booking the baby sitter, a restaurant table, cinema tickets etc)

These issues may seem trivial and ephemeral. Some people tend to think that things will get better as the children get older and their relationships will get

A cool, outwardly healthy young man, Harry is a part-time DJ and aspiring actor – tall and glamorous, with masses of charm. He has come to the clinic with profound erectile dysfunction. Women take a shine to him at a gig and expect him to have sex with them in a shop doorway on the way home. Literally a one-night stand.

Harry can't say why sex is not working. But his background informs me that he needs security, encouragement and affection – the right context with old-fashioned courting which starts with wooing and with sex in the background rather than the foreground.

For good sex he needs to be in a situation where it is safe to fail, and to have control of the pace. It would also help if he were choosing rather than being chosen by girls as a 'sex object'. His situation is so desperate that he cannot achieve sex, despite being the coolest dude in town.

COMMENT
Today, when more young women take the sexual initiative, a man's ego can be easily undermined. The answer is to build confidence through a safe relationship, with sex in the right context of his choosing. The same applies to young women who are pressured and pestered for sex.

back to where it started. However, once the relationship and the sex life have been allowed to deteriorate too much, there may be no going back and the relationship is irretrievably damaged. The risks grow according to the length of time the relationship is ignored.

If one party feels s/he is making all the moves in allowing, showing, telling and taking responsibility, this is likely to build resentment.

7) Mismatch of expectations in the relationship

This is another issue, possibly more intractable. Check out regularly with your partner that you are on the same wavelength.

Some women with anorgasmia may never have experienced good sex, but they expect to get pleasure from their partner who gets the blame for her failure to have an orgasm. People need to take responsibility for their own pleasure, and it is unreasonable to expect your partner to satisfy your unfulfilled needs.

Baggage may be imported from other relationships. A man may expect his woman to act like his mother in the way she looks after him; while a woman expects her partner to be like her father, and behave in the way that her own father did, or did not.

People tend to have inflexible and rigid views of what others are like and how they should behave. Some expectations are unrealistic and this is common on both sides. Men may look for a partner who is fun, a party animal and sexual being, as well as a perfect mother to them and their children; women may want their man to be their lover, knight, nurturer, and decision-maker, as well as a great father to the children.

8) Mature relationships

It is amazing how often the arrival of a child can disrupt a relationship. Babies can become the centre of mismatch and disillusion, driving people to seek a new relationship. Even for mature couples a baby can bring up deep issues. If a man is used to being the 'baby' in the relationship, all of a sudden a new baby leaves no room for him. Commonly women report that they have three children in the family - two kids and the partner. Often this type of relationship works well without children, when the man is the little boy or the woman the little girl.

IN CONCLUSION...

These issues – particularly time and prioritisation – can be settled readily if both parties are committed.

The time issue is a symptom of our society. When you hear couples list what they have to get done in a week, you often find that they have virtually no time left for themselves.

I remember my grandfather working in the docks, maybe for 16 hours a day. But my nan was always at home looking after the home, so they did have time together when he was off work. Many couples today have no time or energy to dedicate themselves to shared activities with each other. They need a regular commitment and priority to give time for discussion, affection, communication and leisure pursuits.

Most couples find this a welcome addition to their routine, a simple ritual with planning, where couples tell each other how much they are looking forward to the set time. This simple process restores and invigorates very many struggling relationships. This applies as much to professional and supposedly informed people as any other section of society.

The life-balance question may be easier to sort out than deeper physical or psychological issues. Deep-seated psychological needs can be a sticking point in a relationship. In these cases both parties need to agree strategies, to avoid continuing to collude with each other's unhelpful behaviour.

Practical Communication Skills for Couples

Virginia Satir, an American family therapist, developed the **Temperature Reading** as a communication tool to help couples and families keep each other updated and to encourage effective and rewarding relationships. She rightly believed that the ability to reveal yourself fully, honestly, and directly is the lifeblood of intimacy.

While this communication tool has been used in many settings, it is perfectly suited to the intimate relationship of a couple. At the clinic, we find that it is difficult for couples who otherwise have good communication skills to communicate effectively around sexual and relational difficulties – almost without exception.

THE TEMPERATURE READING COMPRISES 5 HEADINGS:

APPRECIATIONS

General
Much of the time we hear about what is wrong with us – the world tells us and we tell ourselves all the time; we are usually our own worst critics. This is an opportunity to tell your partner something you appreciate in them.

Hearing appreciations regularly is an important element in our self-esteem. We do need to feel appreciated, valued and accepted by our partners, and self-esteem can also come from outside. It is also important to know what we are appreciated for and to learn to accept appreciation. Many of us have a conditioned response of pushing compliments away – "It was nothing", or "Oh this old thing."

Sexual

It is crucial that we clearly communicate what we appreciate sexually. Our partners are not mind-readers. This includes how we enjoy touch, communication etc. As a general principle it is particularly important to focus on the positive rather than the negative issues in sexual performance. Much better to say 'I like it when you kiss me gently there' rather than 'don't be so rough'.

NEW INFORMATION
General

So much of what goes wrong in relationships is because we are not given the information we need to understand what is going on and there is too much room left for assumptions. When we know what is happening for our partner, it keeps us updated and encourages more satisfying relationships. e.g. "I finally got that new contract"; "There's a good article in *The Guardian* I think you would enjoy."

Sexual

To communicate new information – such as not feeling sexual at the moment, or sore, or neglected – helps your partner to accommodate your sexual needs.

PUZZLES
General

This is an opportunity to ask for clarification e.g. "Why did you seem so edgy this morning?" It is important to clarify questions rather than make assumptions.

The puzzle may be about yourself: "I don't know why I felt so angry when you queried how much I had spent on Christmas presents." Even if you can't find the answers, this process gives your partner some insight about yourself. Besides, your partner may have helpful feedback for you about puzzling experiences.

Sexual

It is essential to clarify with your partner puzzles and questions around your sexual relationship. It is all too easy to personalise events mistakenly. For example, your partner may have been inattentive to your advances for a few nights, and it is easy to assume that they do not fancy you. The reality may be very different. They may be worried about finance or the children, or just feeling low about work or many other issues.

COMPLAINTS WITH RECOMMENDATIONS

General

Complaints should not be blaming or judgmental. You can request change if you really think you need it. In stating your complaint, be specific about which behaviour displeases you and state which behaviour you are asking for instead. For example, "If you're going to be late for dinner, please call me. It annoys me when you don't say that you will be late home from work. That way the children and I can make our own plans and won't be kept waiting for you."

Sexual

While it is important to focus on the positive, as mentioned in Appreciations, it is essential not to neglect the negative. If your partner does something which hurts you, emotionally or physically, do not ignore it. This will damage the relationship sooner or later. State what doesn't work for you sexually and suggest what would work instead. For example, "When you attempt penetration before I am fully aroused it is uncomfortable. Let's agree that I will let you know when I am ready."

Or "When you talk about what you don't like, I feel discouraged. I recommend that you give at least one positive for every negative."

WISHES, HOPES AND DREAMS

General

Share your hopes and dreams. Hopes can range from the little to the large. But the more the two of you bring dreams into immediate awareness, the more likely you'll find a way to realise them.

Sexual

This may provide a forum for exploring fantasy and bits that are missing in your sex lives.

RECOMMENDATIONS FOR USE OF THE TEMPERATURE READING

The Temperature Reading is a nourishing way of keeping each other informed. At first it may feel awkward and clumsy to use and at other times our own low self-esteem may leave us feeling less than eager to make time for this communication.

Positive relationships do not happen by accident. Time needs to be invested in keeping them open and effective and the Temperature Reading can act as a useful tool in relationships when we are willing to make and take the time.

Ensure you have good, uninterrupted time to do the Temperature Reading, and that you have clear time boundaries, e.g. 30 minutes minimum or 60 minutes maximum. It is often a good idea to do the Temperature Reading separately from sexual activity.

Some couples find that a frequency of once a week, or once a month, works well. Others do it 'on demand' when they have a few issues.

* Virginia Satir, 1916–1988, was instrumental in forming the first formal programme in family therapy in the US. She was concerned with the health and healing of each individual human spirit by connecting with a universal life force. Her style came to be based on personal growth. She worked at the Dallas Child Guidance Center and at the Illinois State Psychiatric Institute. Later she helped start the Mental Research Institute in Palo Alto, California, and in 1977 she formed Avanta, an educational organisation to help people change their lives and handle difficulties in their relationships.

She was author or co-author of 12 books, and in *Self Esteem* she wrote:

"I am Me. I own my fantasies, my dreams, my hopes, my fears. I own my triumphs and successes, all my failures and mistakes...I have the tools to survive, to be close to others, to be productive...I am me, and I am okay."

Visit the Virginia Satir Network at: www.avanta.net

Note: For some couples the structured approach of the Temperature Reading doesn't work. A simpler communication tool is a 'Five-a-Side' – when each of you takes five (or ten) minutes to describe an issue that is concerning you. Talk all round the issue; speculate as to where the problem is rooted and what it throws up for you (especially from your past). During this time the other partner listens without interrupting, and at the end can give constructive feedback.

Some of the principles of the Temperature Reading – such as starting with appreciations and always combining a complaint with a recommendation – can be incorporated effectively into a Five-a-Side.

CHAPTER 5

Relationships and having children

Having children – or deciding against it – means a major change in a couple's long-term relationship. There can be considerable benefits for couples in having children. The process of conception, pregnancy, childbirth, and raising children can have considerable benefits for the couple in terms of their relationship, their intimacy and their sexual activity.

It can also raise various issues. Because having children is so special in a relationship there may be some difficulties. So it is important that couples discuss issues arising in a balanced and informed way. I don't want to alarm would-be parents, but tell them about some of the issues which may arise so that they can tackle them constructively.

CONCEPTION AND PREGNANCY

Conception can have all sorts of implications for couples. It may be accidental, or planned and wanted, or not happening. It may have an impact on the relationship and on the sexual well-being of a couple.

It can change the dynamics, and may interfere with integrity of purpose – having sex for sex's sake as mentioned earlier in the book. Having sex in order to conceive may skew the integrity of purpose. A man may feel around conception that his partner wants him because she needs to get pregnant. Some men can have a sense of being 'used' in this context.

John and Jackie who are in their mid-thirties have come to the clinic for some time. John's originally libidinal problems have been sorted out in the clinic and the couple have had a son a few years ago. They want another child but have encountered new difficulties. They complain to me of the palaver of getting pregnant.

In the clinic I tell them, in a matter of fact kind of way: "Well, you don't need penetrative sex. You just need a syringe; the husband masturbates some semen into it, and then you can deal with the problem of conception..."

"That would be one way of taking the pressure off penetrative sex," John agrees with embarrassed laughter. Later in our conversation he returns to the subject of the syringe, musing that this could solve their problem.

Then Jackie surprises us by saying that she likes the idea of watching this activity.

John looks puzzled: "What, you wouldn't mind watching me ... you know?"

Jackie smiles and says softly: "Actually, I think I would rather like it. It might add novelty to our relationship!"

COMMENT
This conversation has helped John and Jackie to conceive another child naturally and that restored their confidence around sex. Remember that trying to get pregnant can affect the integrity of purpose. And human relationships (especially where sex is concerned) often resemble an iceberg where many of the issues lie below the surface and remain hidden to the senses.

During pregnancy hormones may impact in many different ways, such as morning sickness. Pregnancy can affect sex drive, increasing or decreasing it at various times during the pregnancy. It is important for the couple to discuss these changes to ensure that they are not misinterpreted.

For most women and for their partners, some of whom may witness the birth, the whole event can be mainly positive and it is very beneficial to the relationship and subsequent sex. However, the experiences of some women during the birth, or subsequent complications, may impact on the couple's sex life. It is important that they discuss these issues with each other, with their GP, or with a psycho-sexual therapist, whichever is appropriate.

After the birth couples go through many changes in their lives. Issues such as breast-feeding and the sheer busy-ness which a new baby entails – particularly a first child – create massive changes in their routine and their lifestyle. Other changes may arise from one partner leaving work, or both of them sharing the role of looking after the baby.

With such huge changes in their lives, there will be an impact on their sex life, almost inevitably. While they may be closer as a result of all the relationship-enhancing aspects of having a baby, they make love less frequently. With broken nights, reduced hours for sleep, and increased tiredness, the couple may find that access and readiness for sex are greatly reduced, which in turn will impact on the psychological and relational side of their sex lives.

A small number of couples who come to the clinic have found that the seeds of underlying problems in their relationship have been pulled to the surface by the birth of their baby. Couples become so busy looking after their baby that they lose the habit of being sexual with each other. It is important that they prioritise time for themselves to take stock of and explore all the things that are happening to them, to their relationship and their intimacy.

Comment: I strongly urge couples to talk about the changes resulting from having a new baby, comment on them, and try to make sense of them.

MISMATCH IN EXPECTATIONS

There is an increasing chance of a mismatch between their expectations in what they want from the relationship and parenting. This can lead to tensions (see Chapter 9 on Mismatch).

Communication suffers when one of them returns home from work exhausted and wanting to 'chill out' in front of the TV, while the one who has stayed at home craves adult conversation having been with the baby all day. Both can feel left out, ignored, unloved.

CASE STUDY

Edward and Caroline are a professional couple who have had a great relationship, with high levels of intimacy and good companionship. Along comes their first child and they are very happy with their son. Caroline has decided to take full maternity leave to took after the baby.

Soon after their son's arrival they began to argue for the first time. Mystified by this unexpected turn in their relationship, they have come to the clinic to try to end the rows.

I discover that the rows usually erupted with the first hour of Edward's return home from work. When we look at the feelings around this, we find that Caroline is desperate for adult company and information about the world outside the home, where she has spent the day. Edward was tired, and wanted to bury himself in the paper and look at the news to unwind, having briefly acknowledged the baby and said "hello".

They described how they felt 'adolescent' at first in expressing their wants and needs – as if they were saying 'me, me, me' all the time. This resulted in feelings of guilt for both of them.

On exploring this sequence of events in the clinic, the couple reveal that, before the arrival of the baby, they each used to enjoy a period of downtime when they got home from work. Together they decided some strategies: Edward has a set amount of time to unwind, and then spend some time dealing with the baby to give Caroline a break. Then they agreed to enjoy some time together after that.

The arguments have gone away and Caroline and Edward are flourishing.

COMMENT

When these issues arise, it is important to discuss them and find ways to manage them. Edward and Caroline found their own strategic solution, and another couple might agree another tactic. Parents of small children need to manage their needs and put them in order: by setting their priorities, allowing some downtime.

Not all couples have identical attitudes to the importance and place of the children. To one parent the child will be the centre of the universe and they will make all kinds of sacrifices, while the other may be slightly less engaged. Here is a potential mismatch which may cause tensions, because each partner's sense of being a parent differs.

SETTING BOUNDARIES

Another issue which can impact on the couple and their relationship is the setting of boundaries. Most people enjoy sex when it's private, behind closed doors, in the bedroom or a safe place. Children tend to encroach on these boundaries, intruding first by making a noise and later as toddlers when they invade the parents' space.

As the child gets older s/he needs to recognise the parents' need for emotional privacy and private time together in their bedroom on their own. And children need their own private space. So the re-setting of those boundaries is important in creating an appropriate context for the adults' sexual relationship to flourish.

Managing boundaries and keeping good space for adult time together is a challenge, but needs to be addressed to maintain high quality sex and a good relationship. Consider places to have sex or intimacy away from the bedroom, where a warning precedes an interruption by a toddler.

One night a week, which a couple can look forward to, can be enough. It helps couples to resume communicating as they once did, to remember who they are sexually and caring about each other more. All of a sudden the baby stops being the centre of their universe – and that is good for the couple and good for the baby.

CASE STUDY: "THE CHILD MUST COME FIRST"

Nicola is a professional working in a local accountancy practice. Her partner, Vince, a former primary school teacher has given up work to teach their daughter Katie at home. He is convinced that the child's needs must come first. Their five-year-old daughter is allowed to sleep in their bedroom.

Nicola feels that her needs are not being met, but Vince insists on making extra-ordinary allowances for Katie, who is always allowed in the bedroom. Both partners had lost their sexual drive.

In the clinic I find that both of them are devoted to Katie. When I explore the possibility of putting Katie in her own bedroom, both of them take the view that the child's wants and needs are the most important. While Katie is a child, she must come first and her parents must be patient and play second fiddle.

Although in many ways Vince and Nicola have a reasonable relationship with shared values and good communication, I also discover that he is avoiding intimacy, so Katie provides him with a credible excuse.

The first step is to persuade the parents to teach Katie boundaries, so that she will respect their privacy and they will respect hers. As soon as they have understood the educative side of the process, they accepted it as they are a conscientious couple.

Secondly they need to take some quality time together during the week, to talk things through. One of the grandparents agrees to take care of Katie at a regular time each week while Vince and Nicola take a walk, or go out for a meal or just a cup of coffee.

At first Katie objects to the boundaries but she is persuaded that it is better and more 'grown-up' to have her own privacy and to sleep in her own room, unless she has a bad dream or is ill. Gradually, Vince and Nicola learn to prioritise and enjoy their time together, and to restore intimacy. Vince finds that his libido is restored.

COMMENT
Adults need to talk with each other, and with their children, about having privacy and clear boundaries – about the balance of time and space for each other. Parents may become so focused on their children's needs that they forget to focus on each other.

If a child of four or five is allowed to sleep in the parents' bedroom or to walk in and out without boundaries in place, this impacts substantially on a couple's ability to prioritise their time together for their relationship, intimacy and sex.

In the modern world, when a child is born, couples face demands on their resources – physical, emotional, relational and financial. They need to take care and pay attention to having good quality time with each other so that they can maintain a fulfilling sex life while all the other things are going on in their lives.

Childbirth sometimes brings medical conditions, such as incontinence, low moods and post-natal depression. If you have any of these issues, you will find information in Chapter 13. It is important to talk to your GP. If you can't resolve the issue at this first point of contact you might consider making an appointment with a psycho-sexual therapist.

COMMENT

Getting pregnant, having a baby and parenting may all impact on sex for both partners. It is important that they explore openly these issues to navigate this challenging transition. If the issues are continuing to cause concern, discuss your feelings and your medical situation with your GP and, if you need further advice, seek an appointment at your local NHS sexual health clinic.

Preserving, maintaining and sustaining a strong relationship and high quality sex require positive effort and prioritisation. Most people would prefer the stability of preserving their long-term relationship in which each person can adjust, adapt and grow together. This is best achieved by clear and open discussion with your partner and getting medical and therapeutic advice if you are unable to resolve the issues yourself.

CHAPTER 6

Women's physical problems

VAGINISMUS

Vaginismus is one of the more common conditions I deal with in the clinic. It is a painful musculature spasm which affects the entrance to the vagina for about an inch and a half. The muscles contract very tightly and make penetration painful or impossible.

The good news is that the condition is easy to diagnose and we have almost 100% success in treating the problem as long as people stay the course of treatment.

We make a distinction between **primary vaginismus**, where the problem is present before penetration has ever occurred; and **secondary vaginismus**, where the condition develops in a woman who, until this time, has been able to have perfectly normal penetration.

Primary vaginismus is normally discovered in teenage women or those in their early twenties when attempting to insert a tampon or have penetrative sex. The causes are not known.

In approximately half of the women who come to the clinic the condition is associated with them being ill at ease with the sexual parts of their body or having negative attitudes towards sex. Because of their fears surrounding the problem, many of them have difficulty forming or sustaining a relationship. For these women, there are two aspects to the treatment:

1. Work with dilators. This entails using penis-shaped devices starting with a small one and, over a period of time, progressing gradually to a penis-sized dilator. It is advisable to seek advice from a psycho-sexual expert in the use of this procedure.
2. Attitudinal work, enabling the woman to make peace with her body, her feelings about sex, and her relationship.

For the others, there seems to be no apparent cause. Often, the dilator treatment is sufficient to cure the problem.

Secondary vaginismus develops in women who have experienced normal penetrative sex. This may be caused by a variety of factors, including trauma, painful intercourse, or unsatisfactory sex. Trauma can arise from surgery, childbirth, or abuse or rape. In my clinical experience, women who suffer other forms of pain during sexual intercourse often develop degrees of secondary vaginismus. Penetration becomes painful or impossible.

Treatment of secondary vaginismus usually entails dilator work and addressing the possible causes, if they can be identified. Evidence suggests that vaginismus becomes progressively worse because the sufferer anticipates the pain and her muscles react accordingly to worsen the symptoms.

CASE STUDY: VAGINISMUS

Sue, who is 35, has been happily married for 15 years. She and her husband Simon have two children. The first birth was a caesarean due to pre-eclampsia. Sue chose to have a caesarean for the second baby. The referral notes from her doctor implied that she had developed secondary vaginismus.

In the clinic we found that she had never experienced penetrative sex in her life. After reading lesbian literature, she had become pregnant each time by using a syringe to spurt her husband's semen into her vagina (with his agreement). In total it took just five attempts to achieve both pregnancies.

This was a highly treatable case, especially as Sue was not self-conscious and happy to start the procedure. The process included work with dilators and using a mild local anaesthetic and lubricants. She and her husband undertook the work at home as a team.

We had four fortnightly meetings in the clinic, one at each level of using the dilator after the initial meeting. The next step was for Simon to remain still while she lowered herself onto his penis; as she was on top she could control the position, weight, etc and was less likely to suffer pain. She introduced movement over a couple of months.

At the same time they pleasured each other manually and orally so that their sex life remained a sexy and satisfying experience.

Alongside the dilator work the clinic encouraged her to make peace with her body through fantasy, self-stimulation, and reading self-awareness literature.

COMMENT

With vaginismus, women can become alienated from the sexual parts of their body. Making peace with their bodies is as important for them as treating the muscle spasm.

TREATMENTS

In primary cases, many women are not at peace with their bodies. They don't like thinking about their bodies or touching themselves. Whether this is a psychological disposition which has preceded vaginismus or whether it is a response is not known and matters little.

We treat vaginismus through work with a set of dilators. You can get dilators on prescription or buy them inexpensively. Initially we talk to clients about the problem and about dilators. We will probably ask the patient to go and buy dilators for herself, because recently they have become available on prescription. So before we start the treatment they are equipped with information about vaginismus and about the treatment methods.

You might imagine that women with these painful spasms would find treatment difficult, but I find that the direct, clinical approach to the problem often works well. Patients come to the clinic looking for a solution.

The treatment process is undertaken with a woman or a couple working at home. We explain how vaginismus works, with a reflex response like blinking. We are teaching them to 'unblink' as it were. Fighting such a natural reflex – tightening up at the approach of someone or something which will hurt – is difficult, mainly because it is unnatural.

Vaginismus is like going to the dentist. At the dentist we wait for the pain, and the harder we try the less we relax. Similarly we tend to guard old sports injuries and find ways to protect them, which in turn may lead to the injury recurring.

There is an understandable fear of injury from the dilator – that something will break or tear. The barrier of the vaginismus spasm can be particularly powerful after the dilator has been inserted for just an inch – like a brick wall. Local anaesthetics can dull the pain in the first instance and lubricants also help.

We try to ensure that the procedure is as gentle and gradual as the patient wants, with plenty of explanation and reassurance.

CASE STUDY: A COUPLE'S STORY

Anna had known for a while that something was not right with her sex life with her fiancé Chris and she experienced great pain during intercourse. Sexual contact had become more or less non-existent for a long time, mainly because Anna put obstacles in the way to avoid sex.

However a multitude of reasons prevented her from doing anything about it: anxiety, embarrassment, stupidity, and fear of pain. Speaking to her partner Chris was extremely difficult, made worse because she felt sure it was her fault. But, with hindsight, all her concerns probably made the situation worse.

Chris had convinced himself that they had a perfectly normal sexual relationship, until he suddenly realised nothing was really happening. "Anna and I started to talk about the subject from time to time without reaching a solution or even deciding how to tackle the problem. It was always the same old thing that both of us came out with, "Oh, don't worry, things will go back to the way they were before."

Having visited their family doctor and been given a referral to the clinic, tests showed that she had endometriosis, believed to be dormant. This may account for some of the pain during intercourse. "My journey to self-fulfilment was just about to begin, even though it didn't feel that way at the start," Anna recalls.

"Emotionally this experience was incredibly draining. I had to tell a complete stranger my fears, and open myself up to discussing my most intimate difficulties. I think Chris found this hard. But every session he was there, holding my hand however difficult it was to hear, and we began to learn together." Anna found that vaginal muscles would spasm as soon as her body thought it was going to have intercourse, because they associated this with pain.

She adds: "As an individual I have developed both mentally and physically; as a couple we have learnt how to love without it just being about intercourse. However, I could not have done this without Chris, who has been amazing, even though times have been hard. Thank you, Chris, I love you more than words can say."

He was unaware of the pain Anna was suffering during penetrative sex. The revelation caused him feelings of selfishness and guilt. After the referral to the clinic Chris had hoped for a quick solution. "Now I have learnt that there is far more to sex than a quick bit of foreplay followed by penetration!"

"All the pent-up emotions started to spill out from Anna during the first sessions at the clinic and I began to realise what she had bottled up inside her."

COMMENT
This was the start of a long, emotional and physical journey to a better relationship for Anna and Chris. In the process Anna had to learn about herself and self-pleasure. The dilator work and the self-pleasure progressed slowly but steadily. They talk a lot more openly now – the

temperature reading has been a great help in this – and they touch, caress, kiss, and cuddle. Most of their problems have now been dealt with, although there is some work still to do, but I am confident that the remaining issues will be resolved.

DYSPAREUNIA

This is another form of pain which happens during intercourse. The pain occurs around the cervix or the abdomen (rather than the entrance to the vagina, as in vaginismus). It is often caused by lack of full arousal, or by buffeting of the cervix during intercourse.

We treat the pain by helping women to relax, find ways of becoming more relaxed and enjoying sex more fully. In these cases there is often a psychological approach.

However, cases of deep dyspareunia may involve physical pathology, such as endometriosis (pieces of the womb's lining migrate and adhere to the other parts of the abdomen and the ovaries). This can be helped by positioning, and using arousal techniques which are discussed elsewhere. This is again more of a management situation rather than a cure. In the clinic we have found ways for sufferers to reduce pain substantially.

For additional sexual health issues (such as sexually transmitted diseases) see Chapter 13.

CHAPTER 7

Men's physical problems

ERECTILE DIFFICULTIES

Sex is like language. As a species, humans are by nature as profoundly sexual as they are linguistic; every tribe of human beings in the world has language. That language is part of the identity of the users and of their human manifestation. In the same way, sexuality – sexual issues and their expression – is central to human cultures. Of course, this fact does not prevent barriers to understanding other people's language and sexuality.

The language of sex is convoluted, full of embarrassment and hyperbole. Sexuality is defined as the quality or recognition of what is sexual. The dictionary definition of sex relates to gender; to 'have sex' is a colloquialism; and the 'sex act' is defined as 'sexual intercourse' (which is physical contact between humans, as well as penetration). Perhaps we need another word – such as 'sexualness' – to describe the whole essence of sex.

The foulest words in virtually every language known to man are terms of sexual slang or abuse.

The language of sex and sexual problems provokes sniggers and double meanings. I have thought about the term which is central to this chapter – erectile dysfunction.

Fact: UK psycho-sexual clinics report that erectile dysfunction is a primary problem for 50% of men. An additional 13% or 14% report that the main problem is premature ejaculation. The two are inextricably linked. Often premature ejaculation is succeeded by erectile dysfunction.

When an erection is working well, people tend to take it for granted but it is an incredibly complex process. At the physical level it is about blood pressure within certain structures in the penis. The erection involves the brain, the spinal chord, the peripheral nerves, the local vascular system and the endocrine (hormone) system. Indeed the erection is unique in human physiology, and the firmness is remarkable considering it is only maintained by blood pressure.

CASE STUDY: ERECTION DIFFICULTIES DERIVE FROM VAGINISMUS

Bill and Jackie are in their forties and come to the clinic with him complaining that he has problems with his erections. During a lengthy question and answer session, I discover that Jackie experienced a bad sexual relationship in her late twenties, a few years before meeting Bill.

Sex was painful as she suffered from low-grade vaginismus where penetrative sex was possible but painful – this was nothing to do with Bill but the result of an earlier insensitive relationship.

She was trying to conceal the pain for Bill's sake, but he realised that she was uncomfortable and tried to climax quickly when they had intercourse. This precipitated the onset of his erectile dysfunction.

COMMENT
The clinical programme was to treat both Bill's erectile dysfunction and Jackie's vaginismus. The method was to teach the couple to communicate what did and did not work for each of them during sex. She was advised not to put up with any pain and he was asked to say whenever he felt anxious about erectile dysfunction. This allowed them to relax and deal with their problems knowing that they would keep each other informed.

Of course, you can have problems in any of those areas. For example, with diabetes you get vascular problems; and with multiple sclerosis there is often damage to the nerves at a local level.

Common vascular problems include 'leaks' in the system so that you lose the pressure. That is true in people with circulatory problems. It can be as a result of surgery or trauma or general deterioration of the circulatory system, which is common during the ageing process and exacerbated by habits such as smoking and illnesses such as diabetes. There are fairly simple tests to diagnose this.

The cause of vascular leaks from the penis is not fully understood. They are fairly easy to diagnose using angiographic equipment and they can often be treated surgically.

The neural control of the erection is not fully understood. It is not certain which nerves are involved and their precise role. In neurological conditions, the nerve ends may have been damaged through a pathological process, trauma or surgical operation. An operation on a man's prostate, for example, is a classic case where nerves may be pared. Multiple sclerosis and spinal injuries can have an impact on the nervous system's control of erection.

The variability and anatomical distribution of pelvic nerves make it very difficult for surgeons operating on them to be certain of avoiding damage to penis function.

When people are diagnosed with problems like heart condition or circulation or diabetes, they should be asked, and be given, a health check on their sex lives. All these illnesses have an impact on sex in multi-layered ways.

While circulatory problems can affect your ability to have an erection, they can also impact psychologically because your sex drive can be affected by tests and operations to the sexual regions of your body. Besides, worry about your general health is not conducive to feeling good about yourself and your 'sexualness'.

If you have a vascular problem, vacuum constriction devices provide a fairly simple solution. A vacuum constriction device creates an erection and enables a rubber band to be placed at the base of the penis after an erection has been established. This will maintain an erection for as long as needed to achieve good penetrative sex. Seek advice on alternatives for helping with erectile difficulties.

Psychological problems, such as fear of failure, can impact on the erection. The physical and psychological layers interact on each other in a variety of complex ways and can cause problems.

Of course it is quite possible for people to have serious medical problems and yet, psychologically, to feel OK about themselves and their sexuality. Having a medical problem which makes it difficult to have an erection or to maintain one does not mean that you can't have high quality sex.

Men tend to overestimate the importance of penetrative sex, and therefore the need for a good erection; often their concerns are for their partner as well as themselves. And the fact that they have erectile dysfunction may cause men to avoid sexual activity because they believe that penetrative sex is important to their partner. However, many women report having excellent sexual experiences if their man is communicative, loving and affectionate. Lots of women add that they often achieve their best orgasms if this process comes to a climax through manual or oral sex.

Many men fall into the trap of thinking that sex is good and proper only if it spontaneous and penetrative, so, sadly, they avoid all contact for fear of failing to achieve an erection. In the clinic we find that there is a huge gap in knowledge which affects both the sex act and the relationship. When men hear this information in the clinic, it helps them to understand more of their partner's attitudes and sexual needs.

This widespread misconception among men (and women) is fuelled by
* incomplete knowledge
* scripts about what constitutes good sex.

The Psychology of Sex

Humans tend to accept a physical problem more readily because mental or emotional difficulties are less socially acceptable. A person with a physical problem, such as a heart condition or cancer, receives great support, whereas people find it harder to come to terms with a mental health problem or depression, in part due to the attitudes of society.

The perception is that there is something unwholesome – personally unacceptable – about a psycho-sexual difficulty. People prefer to put a health label on a problem rather than admit that it is psychological and something to do with their mental health. Anxiety or stress is put down to personal failing, while a physical illness or condition is acceptable because it is external and 'nobody's fault'.

At the clinic men first want to label their sexual problem as physical, and so fixable. Erectile dysfunction is often associated with a man's loss of power and 'control' – which goes with losing his job or stress or suffering an illness or medical condition.

There are fewer problems for a man with erection difficulties who remains relaxed and realises that this need not impair his and his partner's ability to have fulfilling sex. Indeed he may find that losing the erection and re-stimulating it enhances the sexual process. He and his partner can enjoy more opportunities for varied foreplay. So, loss of erection can become a positive rather than a negative.

I repeat that the biggest dangers for men worried about getting or sustaining an erection are that they:

- avoid sex
- avoid affection (which may lead to sex)
- turn away from their partners
- stop communicating.

The prospect of not having a reliable erection can be experienced as so threatening that the quality of the relationship plummets. This entraps even sophisticated men and women. For many men, the first time they lose an erection shocks them profoundly and, within a few months, they can withdraw from having sex.

Many men are embarrassed by the failure to achieve a spontaneous erection but that is often because they have not talked things through with their partner. Achieving the erection could be a fun thing to do together. Interestingly couples who are prepared to work through the problem together can enjoy sex again, because the psychological elements are nourished and the underlying physical problem has less impact. Whenever a man has a physical problem there is usually a psychological component.

My first question to a man who comes to see me complaining of erectile dysfunction is:

Do you wake up with an early-morning erection?

If you do, you can usually discount most physical conditions. If you don't, we would undertake physical and hormone tests. Early morning erections are a good self-diagnostic tool.

Once you start observing yourself in the sexual act and worrying, it has a self-fulfilling prophecy. The spiral increases if your partner becomes frustrated or unsympathetic; the man will feel pressure and often begin to avoid sex.

When men lose an erection they fear that they won't get it back.

A typical treatment is a start-stop method where men practise bringing themselves to erection, perhaps on their own at first, allowing it to subside and bringing it back. That gives them both control over the erection and confidence, and helps to remove some of the scripts. i.e. When they lose the erection it is gone for good. Rather they can continue to have good sexual contact and go back to it later.

The old myth about spontaneity keeps getting in the way. Don't allow yourself to be suckered into the notion that you aren't a real man any more if you have to do all this work and practice.

The myth of spontaneity is one of the greatest hurdles to good healthy sex

People have a (false) recollection of how spontaneous and easy sex was when they first started. In fact sex is a very intricate and delicate biological system both at intra- and inter-personal levels. It needs investment like any other 'treasured possession'.

It is impossible to exaggerate or be too repetitive about the interplay of the physical and psychological elements of sex. Whether the initial problem is psychological or physical the result will be a rapid deterioration in the man's sexual confidence and performance, often accompanied by a lack of affection and deterioration in sex and the relationship as a whole.

Young lovers

In young men the problem of erectile dysfunction will be psychological 99% of the time. Pressure and fibbing from peers and the media help to spread the myth that young men have an instant erection, at a moment's notice, all hours of the day and night.

However, if a man has a bad experience in his first contact with women he can come to imagine that he will never be able to manage sex, and quickly falls into a downward spiral.

Or a young man might have a neurotic perspective of himself, having grown up in a troubled family where the parents have a poor relationship. Here the word 'neurotic' does not imply that they have a serious mental illness but rather that they are predisposed to worry. This leads to fear, self-doubt and performance anxiety.

Often these individuals are well-disposed to solving their problem because they are sensitive and receptive. Such a personality type brings both strengths and vulnerabilities into the sexual arena.

The habits of young people – alcohol, drugs, lack of sleep, bad diet – can also contribute to sexual problems. These all impact on performance. I get young clients who may be extremely drunk every time they try to have sex – and that is because they may be frightened. Often young people are into casual sex.

If you have a sexual problem, the last thing you need is casual sex. You need a committed, understanding relationship where you can both be vulnerable, take risks and talk about issues – feeling that it is safe to 'fail'. Young people may try a sexual relationship to fix their difficulties, and that is unlikely to work. They need to fix their sexual problems in a good relationship.

Casual sex does not lend itself to dealing with sexual difficulties in a safe environment. While casual sex is often condemned by moral and religious leaders, the therapeutic community acknowledges that it is generally a good thing for young people to experiment to find out what they want. Of course there are health and personal issues to be considered, like sexually transmitted diseases and pregnancy.

Some adults take the view that many young men do not truly grow up until they reach their mid-twenties. So they may not be in a position to enjoy a committed adult sexual relationship until then. It is certainly clear that relationships formed as a young adult may not survive the test of time.

In the clinic we hear frequent reports from older couples about their lack of basic sexual knowledge and failure to experiment when they were younger – often expressed with some regret, even though they would not change their current relationship.

Established or tired relationships

In your Thirties other issues which contribute to erectile dysfunction creep in: tiredness, interruptions (by children), stress with managing the complexities of life, and partners losing each other in the maelstrom of child rearing. So they are not necessarily well-resourced and prioritising good time for sex. To assume that your erection will be there for you and perform irrespective of what is going on in your life is naïve.

The contextual stuff and the neglect of the relationship can contribute to erectile dysfunction. Trying to perform for your partner when you don't feel sexy will make your erection vulnerable. Men in tired relationships are also very vulnerable to erectile dysfunction.

Remember to prioritise sex – to put it in your diary. *I cannot stress that strongly enough.*

People tend to baulk at this or take offence when I suggest it in the clinic, because the approach is too calculating and clinical. But you put other important engagements in your diary, so why not sex? If you don't put important things in the diary – from birthdays to meetings – they slip down the list of priorities unconsciously. That leads to avoidance. So it is not sufficient to keep sex in mind.

I recommend couples with children hiring a baby-sitter for a Friday or Saturday night. Get the children off your hands on some Saturday mornings, when you're not tired and go back to bed. The event doesn't have to be about sex, but starts with good communication and affection – only the couple themselves can work this out.

The aim is to have fun together, to make the 'occasion' quality time. Indeed, if the event is specifically about having sex, that can become a chore. Prioritise the time and context, and it may develop into sex; it is always important for either person to have the chance to say 'no'.

When couples start investing in each other and prioritising good times together, this reverses that downward spiral quickly. Sex is like the rest of the relationship: if you ignore the challenges they will get worse.

Foreplay
Foreplay is another aspect of sex which gets forgotten when people are rearing children. This is not just physical foreplay but preparing in advance. You might call this pre-foreplay, when you phone your partner in the day-time and go out to buy them flowers to take home, letting them know that you find them attractive. You are investing in something which otherwise is lost. This is critical to both parties.

I used to carry a script that I did not flirt any more after I was married. But my wife disabused me. It wasn't that I didn't want to show her affection, I simply thought, "You don't do that any more".

Good relationships require hard work
Habit is also important, and underestimated. Most of us acknowledge, and there is good scientific research, that, if you are having good regular sex, you will feel like it. The hormones for sex are greater; they can be measured in both men and women. When people get out of the habit, the hormones decrease and sex takes more effort.

Good habits make sense from a structural and contextual point of view. If you know that Friday night is a good night for good sexual activity, you will start thinking about it in the week. That is good for you and good for your partner.

You can start talking about it: "I'm really looking forward to this Friday, and what do you fancy?" This should NOT assume an entirely sexual focus.

The over-narrow script

A man is vulnerable if he is worried about losing his erection. If he can liberalise his script and tell himself that it is OK to lose the erection because he and his partner can do different things, the erectile dysfunction fades into the background and is no longer such an issue.

If we can rewrite our scripts, loss of erection becomes something that happens from time to time and is unlikely to be so dysfunctional and disempowering. Your partner can take a positive view of it because it means, say, more oral sex. You can feel good about yourself sexually because you can pleasure your partner.

When you have an erection problem, you can approach it in a number of ways. Try combinations from the list below:
1. Try the start-stop method as described on page 137
2. Discuss it with your partner
3. Speak to a GP
4. Establish or eliminate possible physical causes
5. If the problem is not physical, seek psycho-sexual help
6. Try other sexual expression or activity
7. Consider medical support, e.g. a vacuum constriction device or medication

Exploring these options may seem risky but losing an erection, or not getting one, is a common problem. The good news is that there is a lot you and your partner can do about this apparent problem. You don't need to feel despairing or isolated.

Older males

Sometimes older men have had surgery or they are suffering from health problems. Or their partner may have problems. Two patients in their sixties and seventies came to me; the wife was critical of the performance of her husband (a GP) who had erectile dysfunction. He blamed himself because he could not achieve penetration. The solution? It was a question of the woman's loss of natural lubrication, a common occurrence among older women.

Many men believe that without a hard erection they can't ejaculate; but this is not the case.

It may also be that men no longer want as much sex as they get older. Even if frequency is reduced, the quality and duration of sex can improve with age. Many people enjoy their best sex in the second part of their lives. In fact frequency may increase when men retire because they have more time and energy and less stress.

Unfortunately, many older people suffer in silence over sex, but the clinic finds that GPs and specialists are sending older men for treatment – we are increasingly working with people in their seventies and eighties.

As with the other age groups, much can be achieved, even if the erectile dysfunction is not eradicated. Often the erectile dysfunction becomes less important or the issues evaporate as confidence grows.

Hang on to the fun

Often goal-oriented men are driven by a powerful script to perform. They lose the notion of sex being leisurely, communicative, playful and light-hearted. Thrusting businessmen are judged by achievement, whereas sometimes you need to have a different perspective around sex to flourish and be healthy.

For sex to be good, the man or woman must feel safe to say no, not to want it, or just want parts of it. The whole gamut has to be available so that you can pick and choose exactly what you want.

PREMATURE EJACULATION
Difficult to define precisely, premature ejaculation has several degrees. The problem is often psychological. At one extreme a man ejaculates before achieving penetration. Another typical example results in ejaculation after a short amount of foreplay or sexual activity. Other men say that they reach climax and come too quickly, after only a couple of minutes of penetrative sex, whereas this is acceptable to other men.

The problem afflicts young men who are over-excited and older men who are under stress. And what represents premature ejaculation for one person is satisfactory for another. Of course it also depends on your partner's sexual needs.

The solution is usually found in learning to control the ejaculatory response. One typical method suggested in the clinic is that the client uses the start-stop method (as also used to help erectile dysfunction) – bringing himself close to orgasm and then allowing the erection to subside, and repeating the process several times so that he achieves mastery of ejaculation. Once he has managed this, the same process is repeated with his partner involved, and later in penetrative sex.

This method of treatment tends to be successful. However, if premature ejaculation is not treated, erectile difficulties may follow because the man becomes fearful of having sex.

Retarded ejaculation
In this case it is difficult or impossible to ejaculate. The cause is often physical, For example, an anti-depressant can have a negative effect on the ejaculatory response. It can also be associated with illnesses such as diabetes. More rarely,

retarded ejaculation is caused by a man being unable to let go emotionally or psychologically.

COMMENT
Premature ejaculation can be dealt with effectively in a clinic on most occasions. Retarded ejaculation can often be improved with the help of a psycho-sexual therapist. The solution is sometimes one of management rather than cure.

CHAPTER 8
Libido or sexual interest

DEFINITION

What does libido mean? It can be described as the drive, need, and desire for engaging sexually. Some experts equate it with interest in sex.

Libido is a different issue for men and women, although there is overlap. Often in men libido is specific: a drive towards sex and ejaculating. They believe that they wouldn't start sex without feeling they can complete the process.

Libido is a significant issue, the second most common reason for both men and women coming to a clinic.

In women the libidinal drive or sexual interest can be expressed in a more subtle way, involving the ability to be affectionate, cuddling and having a romantic evening. Keith Hawton writes: "A woman's level of sexual interest may be affected by many factors, especially the nature of her current relationship, her age, her attitudes towards sexuality and her hormonal status, including (at least in some women) the menstrual cycle." *

Libido is a significant issue, the second most common reason for both men and women coming to a clinic. (For men, the number one problem is erectile dysfunction; for women it is pain during intercourse). It is difficult to treat libido because its causes are often multi-faceted.

There are four aspects to problems with libido, although people may experience a complex

* Further reading page 230

interweaving of the key elements discussed earlier – relational, physical, psychological and contextual. One reason why it is so difficult to treat is because you don't miss what you don't want. So individuals often realise the problem when their partner tells them it is threatening the relationship.

Several years into the relationship, with libido in decline, a couple may find it hard to remember why they came together in the first place.

Relational aspects

Most people have few libidinal issues early on in relationships. The problem may arise as the relationship becomes more established and mature. Perhaps one of the couple has a more high-powered job, brings executive behaviour into the home, with less resource and a greater degree of irritability.

The partner feels less valued and senses less energy going into the family and domestic life. Mismatch can develop with the person who has stayed at home wanting to talk about the children and have an adult conversation; their partner is too tired to talk, or has had enough of adult conversation during the working day and wants to switch off.

With both individuals in a different place and behaving in different ways, the fabric of the relationship is undermined. Attraction may decline for one or other or both. This tends to happen gradually, drip by drip, with neither noticing.

Several years into the relationship, with libido in decline, a couple may find it hard to remember why they came together in the first place. Sometimes they believe that they have gone off sex or stopped fancying their partner. They attribute this to a passing phase, part of 'family life' and fail to see the potential cost in their sexual relationship.

At this stage it may become harder for one or other of them to feel that they can ever fancy their partner again. The only solution is to put the relationship back together again, slowly and carefully. In the clinic we will suggest prioritising time for each other and changing behaviour so that they treat each other differently. This involves good communication and giving feedback about what they find attractive (and unattractive) about each other. It may mean that sex has to be put on the backburner for a while.

Some couples have communicated very well over many key issues in the relationship, such as children or finances. But they have put their energy into things other than sex. I reckon that the cause lies partly in the amount we all take on in our lives these days. The roles of many men and women are less straightforward, and both partners may have to juggle their job, their children, their home and their relationship. All this can have a cost.

A couple with libido problems in their relationship may need to take time over communicating clearly, honestly and kindly about what is and is not working, and respecting each other's position.

Love and libido
Love means different things to different people and there are many phases of love – physical, emotional, spiritual, familial, relational. I have not talked much about love in *Intelligent Sex* because I see it as part of the relational whole.

When people come to the clinic with libidinal issues, often they experience themselves as being 'out of love'. They see love as a magical and spiritual feeling, experienced when they were first attracted to one another. When you first fall for somebody, love grabs hold of you, and people assume that is how it will be always; now love has 'gone', they don't see how it can be fixed.

Couples who work at their relationship come to realise that the endurance of love is proportionate to the amount of spadework they have done. Like sex, you need to sustain love with sensitivity and resolve. It may mean not attempting penetrative sex for a while.

Often when libido has gone the man wants sex for reassurance and the woman does not feel like sex; or the man loses his libido because of perceived shortcomings at work, or a loss of self-worth. The one with the lost libido often wants love, affection and attention.

The 'cure' for lost libido may involve a gentle approach to the relationship, with sex sidelined. The couple may need to invest in affection and high quality leisure time together before returning to sex.

Physical aspects
A variety of physical and physiological reasons cause loss of libido. One of them is hormonal. In men testosterone decreases with age; some men suffer a sharper decrease. Usually this will impact on libido. Women have hormonal changes at different stages of the hormonal cycle, and will have changes in their hormones both after childbirth or during menopause. I advise a visit to your GP to check your hormonal profile.

The level of libido differs from person to person. While having sex once a week (or even once a month) is normal for one man or woman, others may want sex every day or at least five times a week. Sometimes people confuse loss of libido with a difference in libido; and they may feel like a different level of sexual activity as the relationship matures and after the first 'sexcitement' of falling in love.

Indeed, when the couple find a good match for their sexual needs, they may well find a rise in sexual needs in the partner previously 'off sex', and a decline in the one with high needs. As I have said, affection and intimacy may be confused with sexual needs. Here I find a gender difference between men and women; whereas some men want sex for reassurance and closeness, women seek different ways to realise these things (and a man may simply have let slip his attention to these important details, which he took great care with while courting).

This illustrates how it is not just the person with low libido who has the problem. It is a case of identifying and defining each individual's normal level of libido.

Libido deteriorates when people suffer other physical issues described in the book: erectile dysfunction, premature ejaculation, vaginismus, painful intercourse, sexually transmitted diseases, other illnesses, and medication (e.g. anti-depressant drugs) which affect sex.

For instance, people who suffer from chronic pain often report into the clinic with loss of libido. Back pain, which is a common complaint, tends to have an impact on your sex drive. Indeed you don't feel sexy if you are ill, in pain or just off-colour.

Libido is often a secondary problem if the physical problem is primary. So men with erectile problems and women with painful intercourse issues tend to have libidinal problems as well. As well as a problem in its own right it often accompanies other troubles. People may struggle on with any of these impediments, and their sexual appetite will be increasingly impaired. And their desire for sex will fall as an instinctive protection against sexual failure or disappointment.

Men who have witnessed childbirth may take a different view of their partner's genitals and lose libido. A woman who becomes a mother can notice a drop in libido with the changing requirements of motherhood (as well as hormonal changes). Motherhood demands a great deal of her practical resources

Psychological aspects
Libido issues are likely to affect men who lose social or financial status through illness, incapacity, lack of success and job loss. Pressure of work can also have an impact. I have talked to many businessmen whose libido has suffered when their company has been through a crisis or when they have faced huge demands. They report a return of libido when they have worked through the crisis and found a measure of success.

Kay and Martin came to the clinic seeking to restore their sex life. Her libido has reduced; the frequency of their love-making has decreased, and she has felt less and less loved in the relationship so less sexy. Kay has sensed sexual pressure, while Martin felt unwanted, and pressure when he raised the matter of sex.

Time has been a major issue in two extraordinarily busy lives. Both in their 40s, Martin runs his own successful business, while Kay works for him part time and brings up two children in their early teens. There is a power dynamic, because Martin set up the business when they were younger and childless. Kay left the company to have children and returned later, but at a much lower level.

She has felt that Martin's goal is to have more sex. In fact quality of physical and emotional contact is more important to him than frequency of sex. She has also believed it wrong to have her own sex life, hardly ever masturbating or developing fantasy.

Part of the work was to help Kay get to know and like her body, stimulate herself, have fantasies, and achieve orgasm on her own. In doing so, her libido gradually rose. Eventually she was able to give herself intense orgasms.

As boss of his business he learned to "throw his weight around". Although a pleasant man he was used to getting his way with employees. Flirting and foreplay with Kay had come to feel 'historic' to him in a long-established relationship. When he re-introduced these activities, Kay felt attractive, wanted and more like reciprocating.

Both began to prioritise, getting relations to look after the children for part of the weekend and ring-fencing time for themselves. Generally sexual activity and the rewards of their sex life improved; so did the quality of their communication and closeness in their relationship. And the couple felt much better about the future of the relationship, which had seemed to them to be rocky when they first came to the clinic.

COMMENT
The clinical work was both psychological and physical. The process was quite slow, involving much talking around the issues during their 12 fortnightly visits. By getting to know her body, and achieve orgasm, Kay has come to feel more in control of her sexual world so she can start reinvesting in the sexual relationship. Martin has had to redevelop his skills around wooing, foreplay, and anger management.

Working with both of them to improve communication clarified their different issues. Once Kay realised what Martin really wanted, she could work satisfactorily with that knowledge and understanding – even with a lower level of libido.

How you feel about yourself psychologically is close to how you feel sexually. If you feel good about yourself, good about your body, good about your work, good about your family, good about your relationships, you will feel better about sex and have a healthy libido.

Conflict or deadness in the relationship will have psychological repercussions on your libido. Similarly grief and loss of a loved one can affect libido. The psychologies of the individuals and the partners intermingle with plenty of attendant psychological issues.

Contextual aspects

Libido can be turned off or down if you have no space, time or resources, or if there is noise and 'interference' from children. An elderly parent who comes to live in your house – and one or both of you take on the role of carer – can precipitate a nosedive in your libido.

Couples are often surprised when we trace loss of libido back to the time when mother or father came to live with them. But they recognise discomfort with the idea that they may be heard by a parent, or it just does not feel right.

CHAPTER 9

Mismatch

Mismatch is a key issue both at a physical and relational level. It is important that couples do not attribute a problem to one person or another but see it as a mismatch between both people.

For instance there can be a mismatch over frequency of sex. One person may want sex five times a week, and the other once a week. This may be framed as a 'sexual problem' – as loss of libido in the person who wants sex once a week, by that individual and/or by their partner.

These are unhelpful issues of definition because they label the mismatch as one person's problem so that individuals feel inadequate or take the blame. If you look at the question of frequency without blame you can start to address how to deal with the mismatch of wants and needs. It becomes an issue for problem-solving between the couple rather than one person's 'failing'. That is usually a more constructive way to deal with it.

Variation in sexual drive and desire is commonplace. But couples come to the clinic complaining either about the other's lack of desire, or about their own inadequacy. Yes, one person wanting sex once a week and the other five times is perfectly normal. And this is not necessarily an issue of gender, with the man possessing a stronger sexual drive, a widespread myth.

CASE STUDY: THE MISMATCHED LIBIDO MYTH

Harry and Jane have an established and successful relationship but he wants sex every day of the week, while Jane wants it only once a week maximum. Both Jane and Harry put this down to her loss of libido.

When we analysed it with them, he didn't simply want sex, he craved affection; his way of manifesting that appeared to be a continual desire for sex. It emerged after a protracted series of discussions that Harry was after a better quality of contact and intimacy in the relationship, and he believed he needed to have sex to achieve that.

Harry's persistent demands caused Jane to withdraw because she was not feeling sexual. A vicious circle was strangling their relationship. The resolution of the problem involved Harry finding new ways to express his need for affection. Jane was delighted to oblige. The consequence was that, when they had sex less frequently, the quality was greatly improved, because Jane was more in the mood. Her libido grew because she did not feel pushed; she started to initiate sex; and she found she could meet Harry's need for affection. So they met somewhere in the middle and solved their problem of mismatch.

A secondary factor in the mismatch was a power dynamic: as a successful businessman Harry felt powerful, but she was disempowered after taking time away from work to bring up children. An interesting upshot of their coming together over sex was that Jane decided to take a teacher training course to enable her to return to work.

COMMENT

Sometimes when you get a mismatch both individuals attribute this to the woman's loss of libido. This is a typical example of mismatch: one person pushes to deal with a relational problem in one way, forcing the partner to move away, and increasing mismatch between them. The issues are further compounded by life changes in work and family. Indeed sex can be a good diagnostic tool for a view of a relationship as a whole.

Men often assume when moving from one relationship to another that their new partner will have exactly the same sexual tastes as the previous one, in terms of frequency, approach, foreplay, position etc. This assumption is likely to lead to mismatch.

AROUSAL MISMATCH

On average men's arousal period is much shorter and that causes a great deal of mismatch. If he does not make sure that his partner is properly aroused or lubricated, she may suffer pain and discomfort and so become less and less ready for sex.

Why men have a shorter arousal time than women is a puzzle but can often cause mismatch. Of course, motherhood and other long-term aspects of a relationship bring with them psychological issues which a man needs to be aware of. This is a question of creating good space for sex, with plenty of warning and pre-arousal foreplay (see the Foreplay section).

AROUSAL MISMATCH

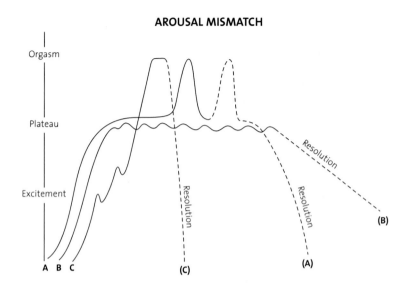

A - A female having one or more orgasms
B - A female not having orgasm but highly aroused
C - A typical male arousal pattern

This diagram illustrates how typically a male may ejaculate before a woman is able to reach orgasm.

SHARING RESPONSIBILITY

Some women (and a few men) carry the myth that it is the man's responsibility to initiate sex and give the woman pleasure. This attitude also causes mismatch, for similar reasons given in the example above, in that it gives one partner too much responsibility for the relationship and the other too little.

We have seen in the case of Jane and Harry how power dynamics can skew a relationship. Broadly speaking, both partners in a healthy relationship need to feel that the other one initiates on a regular basis – not necessarily 50:50 but to a mutually acceptable proportion (it might be 70:30 or 60:40).

The trouble is that many women come to feel disempowered by motherhood which keeps them at home, 'tied to domesticity'. They feel less sexy and so they initiate sex less frequently. This is often compounded by the script "It is a man's role to initiate"; but if the power dynamic shifts to one person, they may start to feel unwanted if the other person no longer initiates sex and responsibility for sex is left solely to them.

CASE STUDY

Mary took the view that her husband Jim was responsible for sex, and their sexual relationship was not working. Given a book on how women can get to know their bodies and give themselves orgasms, Mary returned it, saying it was disgusting and she could not possibly read it because it was against her religious beliefs.

She was challenged to read it so that she could come to terms with her body and learn to be at peace with it. It transpired that she had rarely experienced intercourse and her symptoms clearly indicated primary vaginismus.

However, she and Jim wanted children so the mismatch needed solving. Jim was a very obliging man and colluded with Mary, never stating his wants and needs.

For Mary, sex is frightening and she does it only for her partner's pleasure and to get pregnant. That is a limited and limiting sexual script. Her body won't play with that script until she has learned what she likes in terms of touch and sensation; she needs to train her body over a period of time.

COMMENT
A solution can be found by chipping away at the preconceived notions; sometimes these may be religious, cultural or personal. Eventually this process has enabled Mary make peace with her body and her sexuality.

Family life can lead to mismatch
Family systems can lead to mismatches. For instance, men who are very close to their mothers may run back to their mums, who become over-involved in child issues. If one person sees the wider family as less important than the other, that is another source of mismatch.

There can be issues of single-parent families, where mothers may form an unhealthy relationship with their sons in particular. This has nothing to do with sex, but the son takes the masculine role as well as the filial position, and fills the woman's partnership needs. In the relationship, these sons may not get pushed out of the nest in a full psychological sense soon enough. The same may well apply to fathers and daughters, though I have less experience of this.

This is partly because there is no sexual relationship in the house, and that often helps to move sons and daughters away from home after the age of 16 when they don't fit so neatly in the nest. The adolescent feels angry and wants to leave without knowing why. That kind of teenage tension with their parents is healthy and balanced in the long term, even if it hurts father and mother in the first instance.

Children can cause mismatch between couples: where one person sees them as the centre of the universe and they are free to do what they please and go where they want without consideration for others; whereas the other parent wants to establish boundaries and rules of behaviour around issues like knocking on the parents' bedroom door before entering. In life children need to recognise boundaries and have guidelines about access to other people, and this process starts with their parents.

How parents deal with children can cause mismatch

How parents deal with children can cause mismatch and it is interesting how often the quality of sex or the relationship itself can deteriorate after the birth of the first child. Some couples may have had a mother-son or father-daughter relationship and the arrival of the child usurps the parent's position in that family system.

Cultural differences in partnerships can be the source of differences in how mothers are supported after childbirth, and this creates mismatch. For instance a man who returns home after working abroad with a wife from that culture will separate his partner from her own familial ties and support groups. This may lead to relationship tensions where she becomes under-resourced through loss of social network.

Etiquette and personal behaviour
Families may differ in their attitude to family life, and these differences can be increased by ethnic and cultural influences. Couples may bring to a relationship different models of marriage or partnership. One of the issues presented at

clinics is that women report lack of care in hygiene and dress in men from a different background. When couples are having poor sex, it is surprising how often these kinds of mismatches come to the surface. In the first flush of first love and sex nothing seems to get in the way.

Unrealistic expectations
Some couples accept that they will have different hobbies and friends, but feel their relationship is fine because they are flexible and accommodating. They realise that life is not all black and white. For other couples only a small number of issues can produce a mismatch; they readily see their glass as being half empty. Realistically, you will like many things about your partner, others you will be indifferent to, and some will be abhorrent. The solution is to explore your mutual expectations on a regular basis, and learn to manage the differences which cause friction. That is a real skill in any relationship.

Couples differ in their approach to using tools and books, and learning to manage mismatch and relationship issues. Some prioritise and make changes because they acknowledge that it matters to them. The capacity of an individual and a couple to respond and be flexible is a key indicator of how they will meet up to the challenges in their sexual relations and their relationship in the round.

A Brief Questionnaire on Mismatch

1. How many times would you like sex each week?
   a. once a week   Him ☐
   b. three times a week   Her ☐
   c. five times a week or more

2. Is foreplay between you
   a. too short   Him ☐
   b. sufficient   Her ☐
   c. too long

3. Does your partner do what you like sexually?
   a. nearly always   Him ☐
   b. usually   Her ☐
   c. rarely or never

4. Does your partner engage in fantasies and share them
   a. too much   Him ☐
   b. just right   Her ☐
   c. not often enough
   d. never

5. Does your partner stimulate you physically where and how you like?
   a. all of the time   Him ☐
   b. some of the time   Her ☐
   c. seldom

6. Are there other ways where you feel sexually dissatisfied? (Describe in up to 50 words)

Him _____
_____
_____
_____
_____

Her _____
_____
_____
_____
_____

7. Are there ways where you feel sexually satisfied?

Him _____
_____
_____
_____
_____

Her _____
_____
_____
_____
_____

If this questionnaire reveals mismatch, explore with your partner in a non-blaming way how you can reduce it.

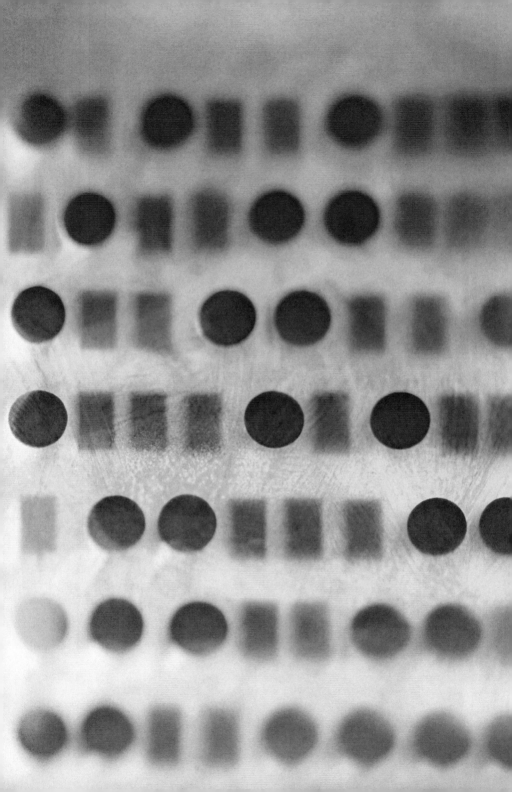

CHAPTER 10

Scripts

What is a script?

A script is a belief or set of ideas or stories, often rigidly held. People think that their scripts are true, although they can be challenged and have their stories modified. Scripts tend to limit choice; this is one of their key attributes.

Is a script also mythical? A script can be a myth, but it can also be true. It has positive and negative attributes. Thus a script may be partially true or true in a particular context. Scripts often come from childhood experience, whereby they are internalised so that we create a map of the world which works for us. Another powerful driver is the critical voice which reacts by saying what is wrong with something rather than what is right.

Typical scripts

Typical scripts apply to many aspects of our relationships and sex lives, including the following

1. Men, about themselves sexually
2. Women, about themselves sexually
3. Sex with a partner – general scripts and myths
4. Penetrative sex
5. Sex in Marriage
6. Masturbation
7. Age

1. MEN, ABOUT THEMSELVES SEXUALLY
The "we are always up for sex" script

Men may carry a script such as "we are always up for sex" – ready for sex at a moment's notice so that they can always perform. This is an onerous responsibility.

What gets a man into trouble is when he is not up for it - this contributes to performance anxiety. Is it created by society or his peer group or himself? That depends on his life experiences, but it will probably be a combination of all three.

Women may collude with this script and you will hear female comments like, "Men are only after one thing". That may be lifted from their mother who heard it from her own mother's generation. This script can cause or contribute to erectile dysfunction.

Men get confused about feeling sexual, and wanting to make love with a woman they find attractive. They confuse desire with arousal and the 'ever-ready' script. It is a perfectly healthy activity to be sexually attracted to women in the street. Fantasy represents sexual good health; but that does not mean that men are always up for sex.

COMMENT

Be aware of scripts, recognise that being ever-ready for sex is an unrealistic myth, and discount it. For good quality sex you need the right context and certain degrees of safety. There are pre-conditions to good sex: desire followed by arousal. Sadly many men attempt to engage in sex too quickly, and when they do not feel properly aroused – which can cause problems.

Andy is a handsome young student in his second year at university. A keen sportsman and attractive to women, he suffers from erectile dysfunction. Andy's script is that, if he and a woman fancy each other, they should be able to jump into bed and enjoy good, penetrative sex.

He puts himself under pressure by expecting to perform casually, at the first meeting, in any context, and under the influence of alcohol – just like many other young men and women in his peer group seem (or claim) to achieve with ease. The circumstances prevent him from performing and so he fails; and failure compounds his erectile difficulties, but still he goes in search of casual sex, banking on one penetrative success to cure his problem. This is a precarious path, almost certainly destined for failure, because he has given himself no chance to get to know or trust women in these casual short-term relationships.

At the same time, he avoids any chance of a more considered relationship, which, he believes, will put more pressure on him to perform. Unfortunately for him, his male and female peer group are up for sex. The females are often much more experienced and do not face the same performance demands.

COMMENT
Andy has come to the clinic to fix a problem with his erection, but he also needs help with relationships so that he can find sage ways to explore and remove the scripts and anxieties which promote erectile dysfunction. For a start he has to bury his pride over erectile failure; secondly, he must sleep with a woman without trying penetrative sex; and then he needs to 'fail safely'. All this requires knowledge, trust and an understanding partner.

I advise Andy to set his sights differently and to tell women that he doesn't like to have penetrative sex on a first date. Playing hard to get can be attractive. Modern attitudes among some women may contribute to masculine erectile dysfunction.

My recommendation to him is to seek a more settled relationship; to tell this partner about his problems; and to say that he wants her help with a clinically approved process to fix it. If the girlfriend agrees and is happy to help him – with relationships and erectile dysfunction – he can return to the clinic, preferably with her alongside him for support.

After a few weeks, he has plucked up the courage to change course and try forming a more stable relationship; he has found a girlfriend who is happy to help. So he feels ready to come back and see me with his current girlfriend.

I advise them to experiment with manual or oral sex, if penetrative sex proves difficult, so that they can enjoy a sexual relationship while he builds his trust and self-esteem. Not long after that Andy arrives at the clinic with a huge smile on his face. The non-penetrative process has removed the pressure to perform and provided him with the confidence to start enjoying penetrative sex. The problems of erectile dysfunction and relationships have fixed themselves very quickly.

The "one sex method works for all women" script

Some men believe that all women can become aroused in the same way. They need to learn subtle sexual skills with each partner; what works for one woman may not work for another.

COMMENT

Recognise that everyone is different; learn from your partner; and experiment. The only person who knows what works for them is the person concerned themselves.

2 WOMEN, ABOUT THEMSELVES SEXUALLY

The "power of penetration" script

Some women hold a script that penetrative sex on the part of the man represents power and makes him more attractive. As a result they feel it is their job to please the man, so they will go along with sex even when they are not aroused (which may be a frequent occurrence). They may tolerate dryness and discomfort during sex, which can lead to conditions such as vaginismus and dyspareunia (pain during intercourse, see earlier section on Women's physical problems).

The "masturbation is immature" script

Many women believe that masturbation is an immature form of sex, and an indication that their partner no longer wants or needs them sexually. They don't like their partner masturbating during a committed relationship. Some disapprove to such an extent that they equate masturbation to their partner being unfaithful.

This script needs to be dispelled firmly. Indeed women who don't fantasise and masturbate on their own, before and during a relationship, are more likely to suffer problems such as painful intercourse, anorgasmia, or loss of libido. This represents a failure to take responsibility for arousing themselves. They have relinquished that function to their partner, and, if she is not clear about what she likes, he is unlikely to get it right.

Masturbation on your own is encouraged, and it can also add to the repertoire of the couple in their foreplay and arousal techniques.

The loss of libido and "something is wrong with me" script

Libido means desire combined with sexual drive, especially from the point of view of internal motivation for sex. When people say they have lost their libido they feel un-sexy. With desire, we mean fancying another, with libido we are talking about motivation for sex. A woman may still fancy her husband but may have lost her libido.

One of the myths about libido is that it's 'my stuff'; 'it's about me'; and 'there is something wrong with me'. The reality is that loss of libido is always about your context, and your partner and the sexual system, unless there is a medical cause.

The "a woman can't be sexy after the menopause" script

During menopause, some women go through a wretched time physically and reckon they will not feel sexual ever again. It is true that, after menopause, many women lubricate less, which causes discomfort, and so they assume that they are becoming less sexual, but there are very good and simple remedies for dryness. And sometimes the elasticity of the skin deteriorates; again many simple applications are available.

These menopause-related physical events can feed myths about the declining sexuality of older women.

There is a myth among men that the menopause means the end of sex for women, but many women report that the best years of their sexual lives happen post-menopause.

Another myth is that women don't feel like sex after experiencing the menopause. This is a difficult period to manage, for women and men. While women may feel unsexy about themselves during menopause itself they may change once they have gone through it.

Some women are truly liberated after menopause: they aren't having menstrual cycles, they have no fear of pregnancy and they no longer have to take the pill. Many women feel at their most sexy during the period of their lives after they emerge from menopause, whereas people can make the mistake of assuming that women don't feel like sex when they are no longer fertile. That is being over-biological. However, hormonal changes may need to be considered during and after menopause. The issues merit discussion with a specialist through your GP.

COMMENT
Report changes to your GP and discuss issues with your partner and a psycho-sexual therapist.

3. SEX WITH A PARTNER
The "sex is your responsibility" script
People who take too much responsibility for their partner's pleasure undermine the sexual process. Many men hold a strong script that they have to please their partner, which means giving them an orgasm. Sex is concurrently a generous and selfish activity in equal measure, and sexual satisfaction comes with balance between selfishness and generosity.

Each individual needs to have their own resources including safety, appropriate context, desire, arousal and so on — and they can't rely on their partner necessarily to provide that for them (although, of course, the partner can help).

Comment: Both men and women are encouraged to take responsibility for pleasuring each other, so the relationship is varied. Women will benefit from taking responsibility for their own fantasy and masturbation. It is unreasonable to expect your partner to give you an orgasm if you don't know how to achieve one for yourself. Couples benefit from open-mindedness about masturbation.

Couples who hold beliefs about joint responsibility for pleasure generally enjoy a much better sex life.

The good "sex needs to be natural and spontaneous" script

It is important that couples who are having regular sex can afford to expect spontaneity. However, if a couple is out of the habit, and has inhibiting factors (such as work and young children), sexual inactivity will become entrenched if they wait around for spontaneous sex to return.

Those couples need to identify when they can spend quality time together, which may or may not involve sex. This is crucial.

At the same time, in the clinic we hear the approach, "Anything about learning or teaching somehow spoils sex". Therapists might tell their clients to prioritise sex and put it in their diaries, just like any other important social engagement. Many couples find this a hard task because it appears to them to demean sex. "If we plan sex, it won't be spontaneous. If it can't be spontaneous it won't be good".

I often allow a couple to go away at this point. If nothing has happened by the next meeting, I point out that waiting for spontaneous sex has not worked, and suggest that they 'book it in their diaries' for a short while. When couples try putting sex in their diary they often find that they improve the health of their sex life; and spontaneity often returns quite quickly.

Avoid judging people by your own sexual habits and tastes. So it is by no means 'boring' for people to have regular sex on, say, a Saturday night or Sunday morning. Predictability may mean that they are prioritising their sex life, which benefits accordingly. Saturday night may be the only time when the partners can be relaxed, not fatigued from work, and free of children.

COMMENT

Foreplay starts before the bedroom. Send messages and flowers. Have a lovely meal. Set a romantic scene. Whatever turns you on. Most of all, prioritise quality time for your relationship.

George and Mandy are in their thirties and arrive at the clinic saying that they have both lost their desire for sex, and can't understand why. George is a policeman who works shifts and Mandy is a part-time nursery teacher.

When I ask them to find one day in each week to dedicate to themselves, they spend 30 minutes going through the days, and eliminating each one. I have to be firm and ask them to go away and find a time when they can invest in their resources and tackle their problems. Something has to go. George decides to give up his regular weekly pint in the pub with his mates, while Mandy agrees to find babysitters for that evening.

Then George and Mandy start to resist on the grounds that prioritising and making arrangements removes the spontaneity which they once had and valued. I remind them that they don't have to use this time for sexual activity; they might choose to go to the cinema or have a nice meal. Having spent some time together, communicating, they might agree to give each other a massage or take a bath together. Quality time creates a context in which communication can take effect and sex can happen.

Down the line, they started to enjoy their evening together, resumed flirting, and indulging in some mild foreplay in advance of each meeting. Once they had recovered the habit of being together and sharing affection, lo and behold spontaneous sex found its way back into their lives.

COMMENT

Here is the classic paradox of a couple avoiding set times because it was not spontaneous or 'good' as they saw it. Yet with habitual regularity came spontaneity.

The "sex should remain as it was when I was falling in love" script

Sex is a highly complex issue, and you ignore the complexity of sex at your peril. At 19 we 'fall in love perfectly on sight' and think that, somehow, sex and attraction will be like that forever.

Clinical experience shows that, in sexual relations, anything is possible. Some couples begin with fairly mediocre sex and it gets worse or becomes better; others start with huge sexual chemistry and sex becomes mediocre slowly -– or quickly.

I have never known a couple where the quality of sex doesn't change at some point in their relationship. This is where the work and maintenance come in. Couples who have stayed in love and continue to enjoy sex have usually put in a lot of practice, either consciously or unconsciously.

COMMENT

You have to work at sex. If the sexual relationship feels 'difficult' accept this stage as part of the 'reality' of your relationship. Then, you will find the relationship easier to manage and to improve. It takes energy, thought, resourcefulness to achieve and sustain a good relationship, and that does not happen by chance.

The "sex is a serious business" script

There is a script that sex has to be special and romantic with soft music. Sometimes this formal approach can take the fun out of sex, which can be playful and experimental – an image which is rarely portrayed. Often sex is all kinds of silly things, in ludicrous contexts.

COMMENT

Experiment. Try different things. Discuss with your partner aspects of sex you find uncomfortable or unappealing, and offer some alternatives. Tell your partner what you want and see if you can agree a way forward.

4. PENETRATIVE SEX

The "Good Sex = penetrative sex" script

There is a belief (apparently held by President Clinton) that true sex means penetration, ejaculation and orgasm, sometimes by both partners. For many of us penetration is a deeply rewarding aspect, psychologically and physiologically, but it is only one version of sex. We would not want to take anything away from this. However there is no foundation in the script that 'Proper sex= penetration'.

Overly defining sex as a penetrative pursuit can be bad news for men because it leads to performance anxiety. Most people who have good sex acknowledge that penetration is only one aspect of it. This script is also bad news for women who seldom achieve orgasm during penetrative sex but can achieve it easily through clitoral stimulation.

COMMENT

Find a balance. Discuss with your partner which sexual activities are most satisfactory and pleasurable for you and them.

The "Erection = arousal" script

This script has many elements, some of them age-related. The first issue is that you can have an erection and not be sexually aroused. That is difficult for men to grasp. Men can have early morning erections, especially when they are young which have nothing to do with sex. This is a physiological phenomenon which is not necessarily related to arousal. You can feel distinctly unsexy and still have an erection. This is important for women to realise.

Many men avoid expressing desire if they are frightened that arousal won't follow, and yet their partner would appreciate the expression of desire and find it very valuable. If they know their husband is anxious about getting an erection but still fancies them they will be happier than if they did not have that information. A woman may assume that, if her partner is not aroused or touching her, he no longer fancies her any more, whereas he may simply be avoiding embarrassment. Men with erectile problems often stop performing loving acts with their partner.

Interestingly men's arousal is often highly visual, but they can feel aroused and sexy and ejaculate without having an erection. When men don't have an erection, they may assume they are not up for sex.

Many men avoid foreplay because they don't have an erection so they don't think sex is viable. Failure to engage in good foreplay is highly likely to contribute to erectile dysfunction.

The other side of this is that a flaccid penis can be very sensual. However, some men are scared of their partner making a fuss of their limp penis, caressing it and playing with it, because they don't know where the process is leading and whether or not they will be able to perform. Enjoying the sexual journey rather than worrying about the destination, or how you get there, is an important state of mind.

Women don't have the same performance issues, and they can allow their partner to have a nice time and feel they are being made love to.

COMMENT

From the age of about 40 men will find that their spontaneous erections become less regular and they often assume that, consequently, they are less interested in sex. A healthier script is to enter into foreplay and see where it goes. Foreplay may progress to full penetrative sex, and it may not. However, it is a good sexual game to practise. Liberalising the scripts is very important and crucial to men as they age.

Many of the scripts outlined in this chapter undermine a key prerequisite of good sex: that you must desire the other person.

Here is a healthy attitude to develop:

For sex to stay healthy you need an appropriate measure of these three factors in the right sequence.

Desire – Arousal – Sex

You can stop at any point of this chain of events. So you can enjoy desire and arousal without automatically having sex. Sexual difficulties may arise if you try and short circuit or alter the process, by cutting corners in this basic axiom of sexual activity.

Make sure that all three are in order and don't short circuit them.

Remove and resolve obstacles such anger or frustration from other parts of the relationship.

5. SEX IN MARRIAGE
The "no flirting in marriage" script
The peripheral activities around sex may decline after marriage or childbirth. The notion of flirting and foreplay may stop because you assume you don't need it in an established relationship

CASE STUDY

A mature professional couple in their early sixties are approaching retirement. Geoff is a senior lecturer at a university and Sheila is active in the local branch of a large charity. She looks 10 years younger and wants sex, although she has been through the menopause. Geoff has an apparently mild case of erectile dysfunction and avoids sex. He has stopped being sexual.

Trying to get involved in flirting and making a fuss of his wife makes him feel foolish. He has got out of the habit. Interestingly she tolerates him cracking off-hand jokes in the clinic. I tell her I would be hurt by his attitude and invite her to take more responsibility by expressing her feelings towards his aggressive and dismissive behaviour whenever flirting is mentioned. He has become a naughty little schoolboy, with humour to match, whenever we talk about sex.

I point out to Geoff that part of his role as a man is to show Sheila that she is wanted and desire and loved, and to make the relationship sexual at many different levels. He thinks he is past that and his erectile dysfunction compounds the problem. By restoring flirting to rekindle the desire and arousal and sexual activity, this should in turn restore the relationship as a whole.

We have used the start-stop method to increase his control over ejaculation and prescribed a course of Viagra so that Geoff has become more confident about entering the flirting process and is embarking on penetrative sex. And we have undertaken some mentoring with both of them to ensure that they have clean and clear communications and can rebuild their relationship.

Geoff has to realise that, for sex to happen, he must be sexual with Sheila. His script is that he feels wretched because he can't perform and has a fear of rejection, so won't take risks; Sheila is low because she feels unwanted.

COMMENT
I encourage clients to face up to their fears and acknowledge the impact of each other's behaviour on the relationship. Be firm about not accepting unkindness in the relationship.

The "Sex only happens in the bedroom" script

Communicating outside the bedroom contributes to the health of the sexual relationship. Even the bedroom as the place for sex is both a script and an issue in marriage. Given safety and desire/arousal sex can be fun in any place and at any time. However, after marriage, particularly with children around, the contexts will change.

COMMENT

Couples find dividends when they accept diversity and novelty and give themselves permission to explore. It is part of recognising how contextual sex is. A couple need to spend time discussing context – and sex outside the bedroom.

Script issues around childbirth, having a family and children

After marriage, particularly with children, some contexts and scripts will change. Breast-feeding the baby may make breasts less sexual for men as well as women. People internalise feelings about parenthood: your parents are not seen as 'sexual' beings; therefore being a parent may be viewed as less sexual.

Children may become the centre of the universe, to the detriment of their parents' sexual relationship. From the good practice point of view, children need to learn boundaries about their parents, about society and about privacy. Parents need to allow themselves good time and space where children are involved. See Chapter 5.

COMMENT

Deal with the issues with your children with good clear accepting boundaries which send messages that your feelings are positive, and there are private things between parents which are good and enjoyable. It's about language and body language. Remember that children are learning about boundaries when the bedroom door is closed to them; and learning that parents have important needs is good developmental training for children.

6. MASTURBATION

The "masturbation is for single people only" script

This can be a script for both sexes. Familiar scripts carry old sayings such as "Wanking makes you blind" and "Glasses are the sign of a mis-spent youth". Some men think masturbation is naughty or pathetic. To call someone "a wanker" is a term of abuse.

In fact, masturbation, as part of fantasy for men and women, can indicate a healthy sex life. Some men and women carry a script that, if a partner is masturbating without them, this is a comment on the inadequacy of their relationship.

Married women may decide that masturbation and fantasy are no longer appropriate and it is their husband's job to give them pleasure/orgasms. If you don't understand your body well and have your own fantasy world, it makes it harder to have good sex – and you shouldn't blame your partner.

The "vibrators are addictive and will damage your sex life" myth

Some women believe that learning to masturbate pleasurably with vibrators will be addictive and detract from their sex life with their partner/husband. There is absolutely no evidence to support that. The healthy approach is that what you learn from masturbation you share and weave into your relationship.

COMMENT

Masturbation makes a positive contribution to your sex life because it helps you to know your body and express your sexuality.

7. AGE
The "people become less sexy as they get older" script
As men age their capacity for a spontaneous erection declines, but their capacity for sex may not. Indeed their capacity to engage in sex for longer may increase through practice and turning the volume down on the importance of penetration and ejaculation. As a result the change can be qualitative and quantitative; and they could be engaging in better sex.

Older women have a varied profile. After menopause many women feel more sexual because they know they can't conceive; and they feel better when there aren't children around – children are an inhibitor, partly because the safe space and resources are reduced. So it is sad if the older woman is feeling more sexual while her husband/partner is the opposite; so they can miss each other.

The "it is inappropriate for an older woman to have sex" script
Another script prescribes that it is not appropriate for older women to be sexual. People are bombarded with images about attraction and they are nearly always related to youth. These images must be internalised at some level in all of us.

COMMENT
The ageing process has a different impact for the sexes, but both men and women can enjoy good sex. Many older women need reassurance and encouragement to 'own' and enjoy their sexuality.

Note: This book does not tackle scripts concerning transcultural issues or same gender sex.

CHAPTER 11

Other issues

OBSESSIVE BEHAVIOUR
Obsession is defined as a behaviour where people spend considerable resources, time and money at the expense of themselves and others. This has a detrimental effect on their health and well-being. It may also have an impact on their relationship and on their sex life.

Various types of behaviour undermine the integrity of a relationship, including sex. Examples of obsessive-compulsive behaviour may involve affairs, alcohol, drugs, the internet, prostitutes, work, and gambling. Even parenting seems to have fallen foul of the obsessive-compulsive syndrome.

Tackling such problems allows relationships to move forward constructively by finding ways of rebuilding trust and coming to terms with where the relationship is not working.

AFFAIRS CAN BE OBSESSIVE
Affairs can derive from a form of obsession. In the hospital clinic I work frequently with couples where one of them has had an affair. Usually an affair indicates that the long-term relationship does not meet the needs of one partner. While someone may be devoted to hedonism and their own pleasure, it is more likely that there has been a breakdown in communication – either they are not revealing their needs or their partner is not listening.

Most relationships are vulnerable to an affair when they stop working. The notion that 'affairs just happen' is usually false. People rarely have affairs if they are enjoying good communication and excellent sex in a long-term relationship. The best way to re-establish a good relationship is to free yourselves from blame, guilt and punishment. You need help almost certainly. When you are in a failing relationship you are not always the best judge of whether it is fixable. A relationship may feel hopeless, but solutions can be found when the problems are identified.

If you have children living at home (of any age), spend more time prioritising your relationship. If it goes wrong, try to fix it by investigating the relationship and seeing whether there is something to save. The most likely causes of relational problems are lack of communication and responsiveness, and that can be fixed. Take several months to discuss the issues and work on a strategy with a sexual and/or relationship therapist.

This requires the two people to examine the issues between them and let go of past issues so that they can move forward. This process is often complex and usually benefits from the clarity and distance of a professional helper. In fact, couples that come to clinics for advice, and work on their relationship, often find that they can establish good structures and move on, to a better relationship.

I am not taking a high moral stand about affairs, and relationship breakdowns, or suggesting that you flog a dead horse. But surely a long-term relationship is worth some problem-solving attention to see whether you have something worth saving – in your own selfish interests if for no other reason, and particularly if children are involved.

Think of the high cost of separation and divorce for the individuals (whoever instigates it), their children, family, relations and friends.

The downside of separation and divorce is potentially damaging and enduring, both for the individuals and for those around them. Experience shows that the break-up of a long-term relationship may affect the people involved for many years. Family events (birthdays, Christmas etc) may cause divorced and separated individuals to revisit issues which they thought had been settled.

ALCOHOLISM & DRUGS

Abuse of drugs and other substances fall into the same category. Growing up and living in a family where there is alcohol or drug abuse teaches you collusion: alcoholism is never mentioned; secrecy and denial prevail; you find yourself walking on eggshells.

However, it is never helpful to collude with an alcoholic in a relationship. The issue needs to be faced and brought to a head.

If your partner has a drink or drugs problem, lay down the law and say that this type of behaviour is NOT OK. People often try to carry on; their alcoholic partner gives promises which are not fulfilled; and this wears people down. Love and understanding in a relationship never solve the problems of alcohol or drugs.

It's hard to think of a good relationship where abuse of drugs or alcohol are involved. Reality takes a back seat, and the non-addictive partner is trapped in the tricky and dishonest world of the addict. There's a thin line between 'alcoholism', 'heavy drinking', or 'over-use' of alcohol, and the addict weaves along it, often with impunity.

Be brave, get help, and challenge a partner who is prepared to undermine a relationship for the sake of a habit.

OBSESSION WITH THE INTERNET

The internet snares people who tend towards obsessive behaviour. Online porn is reminiscent of the compulsive obsession with fruit machines, where the machine and its owner are the only winners. It can affect both men and women.

Sampling pornography for the occasional fantasy, or leisure pursuit, is a different matter, and encouraged elsewhere in the book. However the obsessive-compulsive person makes online pornography an excuse for avoiding contact with their partner. Those obsessed with online porn find the habit hard to kick, wasting their libido in front of the computer rather than in the bedroom, and spending piles of money on their credit card. The costs are considerable, spiritually, sexually, relationally, financially and in terms of time.

Part of the reason for this rising trend in obsessive-compulsive behaviour is the pernicious ease of access of some online leisure pursuits. The obsessive-compulsive personality is readily hooked by using the internet.

CASE STUDY: FLIRTING ON THE INTERNET

Philippa's relationship needs were not being met; so she found the internet a useful outlet and started flirting in chat rooms. She came to the clinic for psycho-sexual advice because she was concerned about her growing compulsion to use internet chat rooms as a place to flirt.

She saw her obsession as her own problem and came to the clinic without her husband, Tom, a farm-worker with uncompromising views (which were partly fuelled by his own parents). He was furious with Philippa's activities on the internet; found it hard to talk about the problem, meet her relationship needs, or forgive her. The move he needed to make was to accept that her behaviour was, in part, a symptom of their relationship (it did not pre-date it).

Eventually Philippa did manage to get Tom to accompany her to the clinic. It soon became obvious to me that, although he loved her, he did not want to admit that he was under stress at work and felt too tired for intimacy. So, we worked on building up his libido while we were tackling Philippa's addiction.

Tom was persuaded to devote some priority time to talking to his wife, for at least 10 minutes every day and for longer on Fridays or at weekends. These were agreed times for closeness and communication. Gradually their physical intimacy was restored, and at the same time Philippa's addiction for internet chat rooms faded. Her need for flirting was met at home.

COMMENT
Seek help from a psycho-sexual therapist before too much damage is done.

WORKAHOLISM
Maintaining and improving a good relationship requires careful prioritisation of time, space and effort, with each individual in a receptive and supportive frame of mind to meet their partner's needs and wishes as a human being. Work can disrupt this important process.

The personality downside to success at work may be significant. Women often report in the clinic that, as some men climb the ladder, their irritability increases and their availability as a partner decreases in proportion to their business success.

The couple need to find ways of creating high quality time for each other – listening, hearing, and becoming good problem-solvers. It's a challenge to find time for your relationship when you have kids, demanding jobs, and a full social life. Statistically the working week in the UK is longer than in other parts of Europe. When you add up all the different things people do in a day, little time seems to remain for the couple's relationship.

Generally, women are good at switching between work, business and partner mode. Men need more time to tune in before they become sociable and receptive. This may be the result of the socialisation of women who get used to holding several balls in the air – work, children, home, friends, hobbies etc. Child-rearing requires phenomenal multi-tasking skills.

Couples whose kids have just flown the nest often tell the clinic that they don't know each other sometimes. They are unsure whether they are still 'properly married', whether they want to stay married, or what their relationship might be like without children. Couples talk of 'meeting each other' all over again, and they have to start with a clean sheet. Time is one of the biggest deficits in relationships.

CHAPTER 12

A working week in the life of the clinic

I work as part of a team in the psycho-sexual unit of a sexual health clinic in southern England. Couples and individuals with sexual difficulties are usually referred by their doctors, or internally from various hospital departments.

At the clinic people feel free to open up and become more honest with themselves and with their partner. This can be hard at first, but when people persevere they often get considerable rewards – and find long-term solutions – from openly discussing their sexual and relationship problems, and undertaking exercises and treatments.

If you have any concerns about your sex life, consult your GP and ask to be referred to the nearest psycho-sexual clinic in your area. Whether your problem is physiological or psychological or relational, a clinic can often help. You might visit the BASRT website (see Chapter 14 on Resources).

The skill of the therapist is to create a safe environment to open up and give permission for exploring the emotional and physical boundaries which hold people back and prevent them from enjoying a full relationship. The relative anonymity and unfamiliarity of the therapist enables people to share their thoughts and feelings in ways which may prove impossible with family and friends.

People have a marvellous capacity in the clinic to share with the therapist, a complete stranger, the sexual, physical and relational problems which they don't tell the person they know so well – and have slept with for years!

Here are 5 case studies to illustrate a typical working week in the clinic. They highlight the need for clear two-way communication, which involves listening and blame-free discussion.

1. CLEAR COMMUNICATION PUTS CHANGE IN CONTEXT
A shift in the context of a relationship can throw up new problems for a couple. When the context changes, your libido can suffer, however much you think you like the new circumstances.

Adam and Zoe are a loving young couple who seem to have everything going for them. He has a great new job and they have moved into a flat, which Zoe tells me is 'lovely' and 'what I always wanted'. She came to the clinic originally with vaginismus and the treatment has gone well.

Suddenly Zoe loses her libido again and her vaginismus returns. At first, this case seems contradictory with so many positive factors going for the couple, but further questioning reveals some hidden issues. For the first time, Zoe, who is close to her mother and father, has left her parental home, where she has her own bedroom and still keeps some of her prized possessions. The bedroom in the new flat does not seem to belong to her; and she has lost her sense of space and privacy.

The first step is to establish closer communication between the couple: Zoe needs to reveal her sense of loss to Adam; and he has to express his disappointment that she lacks sexual energy, and that the progress on vaginismus has halted – without putting pressure on her to perform.

Adam's disappointment and concern has proved more affirming than if he had stayed quiet, and seemed not to care. He understands Zoe's feelings of loss. Clarity of communication enables her to resolve the physical issues from vaginismus, and brings the couple together, improving the quality of their sex life.

COMMENT
Expressing your feelings usually has positive results, as long as you listen carefully to each other and create space for dialogue and feedback. If things change in the quality of your sex life, look at what has changed in your life and what impact they may have.

2. LEARN TO SEE THE BIG PICTURE
A man's erectile dysfunction and his wife's promotion may represent a small section from a large picture

Dave, a jobbing electrician, has paid several visits to the clinic to tackle his erection problems. Although he has had some success with self-stimulation, he remains reluctant to make sexual advances to his wife Denise. If he manages to get an erection and goes for penetrative sex, the activity tends to be short and bitter sweet – functional at best and not satisfying for either of them. This adds to his pressure to perform.

Meanwhile Denise is feeling more confident and sure of herself after promotion to assistant manager at work. Dave finds this hard to take, and he has two other issues on his mind: 1) A favourite aunt has died. 2) He has been involved in rescuing a work colleague from a dangerous situation in a house which suddenly started to collapse. They both escaped to safety but Dave is suffering from post-traumatic stress.

As a result of all this, his erection problems have returned to haunt him. His libido has hit rock bottom. His own life experiences and Denise's new-found confidence through her job changes have produced a different set of circumstances to challenge the relationship.

At the clinic we uncover the underlying issues for Dave – the bigger picture. We also discover that Denise's deepest needs are for intimacy, closeness and a feeling that she is desirable. So Dave is asked to concentrate on foreplay and to set a specific sexual target – not to have penetrative sex until his erection problems improve. When Dave engages in foreplay he continues to want penetrative sex, but Denise insists on sticking to the ground rules and forbids it.

The scenario of 'forbidden sex' provides a frisson, a new sexual energy which was not present before, and removes the performance pressures from Dave. He also finds that he can be sexy without having to perform, while suffering masculine frustrations around wanting sex and being denied.

We also ask Dave to check out his levels of communication and response with Denise. He has to repeat back to Denise what she says to him so that she knows he has both listened to her and heard her (the two things are not the same).

In fact his responses to her have been valid, but at first he discounts the process and describes the exercise as 'rubbish'. However he comes round because Denise expresses her delight that he listens to her, hears her and provides positive feedback. Slowly, their relationship, their communication and their sex life go from bad to good, and Dave's erectile problems are largely solved.

COMMENT
Always look for the bigger picture and ways to communicate your experiences to discover a brighter and better sexual life. Don't underestimate the impact of contextual issues, e.g. the death of a relative or an accident.

3. ANGST AFTER AN ACCIDENT
Post-traumatic stress after a man's car accident has a serious affect on his partner's libido

Jeff is recovering after a horrific accident in his Mini Cooper on the way to work when he broke his right leg in several places and spent two weeks in intensive care. Jeff and his partner Jenny have come to the clinic because he feels ready for sex, but the couple cannot find a way through her libido difficulties.

Jenny initially expresses concern about hurting Jeff's injured leg, but soon we discover that she is worried deep down about him using the Mini Cooper again. We face a power dilemma: Jeff wants to drive, but Jenny is scared about his safety.

So we have to alleviate her fears without taking away his freedom to drive. There is no simple 'black-and-white' solution. The couple are encouraged to talk and agree some ground rules around his driving, which will leave her feeling safer. So, he promises to obey speed limits and to contact her reassuringly as soon as he reaches work.

COMMENT
Practise your listening skills. Sometimes people stay within their own agenda and leave no room to hear what the other person says. They do not hear each other. A couple may have to repeat this process several times before they get it right but this 'skill' can be achieved comfortably with practice.

4. UNDER PRESSURE
Being chased for sex by rampant young women isn't necessarily every man's dream come true.

Ben, a student, comes to the clinic bemused by his inability to perform sexually. He has managed sex with the help of Viagra on a few occasions, but he recognises that this is not the way forward.

His attempts at quick sex provide the exact circumstances which doom him to disappointment. Only sexual encounters in a good context will help, while high-risk sex sessions in vulnerable situations will continue to undermine his confidence.

What Ben needs is a better relationship in safer surroundings with someone he truly likes. However, he has resolved against entering a serious relationship with any woman until he has fixed his sexual problems – he first wants to manage what matters to him, i.e. being able to perform.

The clinic suggests that Ben sets some simple ground-rules: removing casual sex from the agenda and being intimate in a safe context with a sympathetic partner of his own choosing who can help him with his problems – without penetration to start with.

The case is an example of sex which is 'unsafe' in terms of emotion and context – a form of intimacy problem. It shows that men are vulnerable, and that their sexual apparatus does not always work on demand, unless the context is right.

COMMENT
Erectile dysfunction is best addressed in a safe and understanding relationship where it is safe to 'fail'.

5. ONE SEX CURE MAY PROVOKE NEW PROBLEMS

Correcting sexual problems may cause shifts and rifts in a relationship, because the solution to one person's 'inadequacy' brings other relational problems to the surface.

Mandy is a young woman in her late twenties who suffers from vaginismus. She tells me that she has suffered from shyness for as long as she can remember; that she is unhappy with her appearance, and self-conscious about her large breasts.

I encourage her to make peace with her body and discover her preferences for touch and pressure, through a course of treatment using fantasy, self-stimulation and vibrators. She makes good progress towards curing her vaginismus, and her sexuality begins to blossom.

Mandy has also re-trained as a lawyer and found a responsible job. Her sexual awakening, combined with her new job, have increased her self-confidence. In the process, she discovers much dissatisfaction with her partner, Mike, and their relationship, which started more than seven years before. He was once in the police force, but now has a job which is both less satisfying and remunerative.

When she acted shy, awkward and timid, they rubbed along together. Now he behaves defensively in response to her increased confidence and assertiveness. The dynamic of the relationship has changed. This has manifested itself in bouts of irritability and petty squabbles.

As a result, Mandy ceases to make progress with the vaginismus treatment, and their relationship is floundering. They report to me their dismay at this new argumentative and unhappy turn in their relationship. Their latest row has been about a vase, which Mandy has made at evening class and which Mike has broken.

She has fumed at him, and at first he has denied causing the break – a typical pattern. Clumsiness is one of Mike's admitted 'faults'. He sees himself as habitually clumsy but he never talks about his blunders and leaves Mandy to find them out for herself. The broken vase provokes another row, at a childish level of accusation and denial – "Oh yes you did break it" and "Oh no I didn't".

I advise them to address their relationship problems by learning to communicate through a regular 'Temperature Reading' – (see Chapter 4 for more detail) which involves the couple in the following series of two-way discussions:
- **Appreciations**
- **New information**
- **Puzzles**
- **Complaints and recommendations**
- **Wishes, hopes and dreams**

Mike and Mandy agree to have a Temperature Reading every day for two weeks. And Mike promises that, as soon as he has done something clumsy round the house, he will talk to Mandy about it; and she pledges not to play the blame game with him. On their return to the clinic, they report that communication had improved hugely and that Mike has been less clumsy.

This process of communication has been extended to their whole relationship, including sex, with positive results.

COMMENT

Use the Temperature Reading process regularly to keep channels of communication open. Talk openly about changes in the relationship that result from substantial change, e.g. Career.

PART III:
REFERENCE & HELP

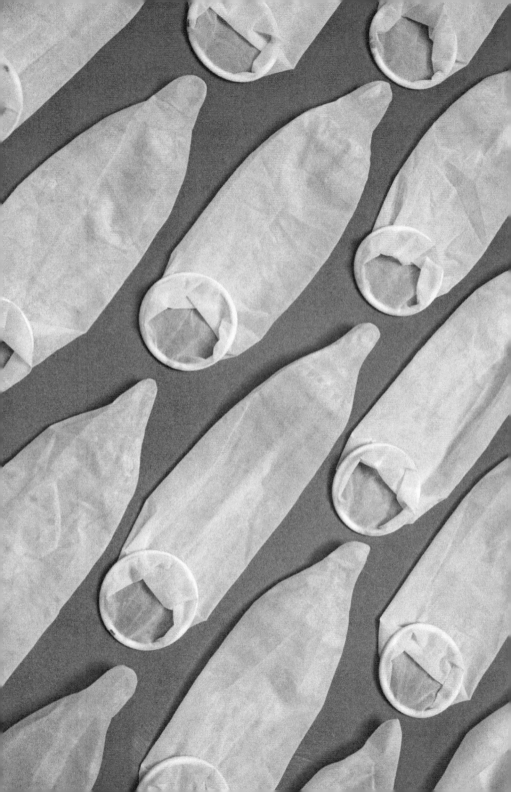

CHAPTER 13

Contraception and Sexual Health

CONTRACEPTION

If you want advice or information on a contraception method, you can ask your doctor, practice nurse or family planning clinic. Alternatively you can ring the national office of the Family Planning Service (formerly the Family Planning Association), or visit their website at: www.fpa.org.uk

If you prefer not to go to your own general practice, or they don't provide contraceptive services, they will give you information about another practice or clinic. All treatment is confidential and free.

There are many contraceptive methods. None of them is perfect. All contraceptives have an impact on sexual well-being. Sometimes the impact can be positive but often it is negative.

A list of possible contraceptive methods is given below.
- The combined pill
- Contraceptive implant
- Contraceptive injections
- Contraceptive patch
- Diaphragms and caps
- Emergency contraception, e.g. the 'morning-after pill'
- The intrauterine device (IUD)
- The intrauterine system (IUS)
- Male and female condoms
- Male and female sterilisation
- Natural family planning
- The progestogen-only pill (POP)

It is important to evaluate your options as a couple before starting contraception. It is also important to evaluate its impact periodically. Don't hesitate to go back to the health professionals if it is not working for you at any level.

Many couples use various forms of the contraceptive pill as a *safe* and *convenient* method of contraception. Various versions of the pill can have side-effects, including weight gain and loss of libido. Recent research shows that women often have depleted levels of testosterone for many months after ceasing taking the pill. This will have an impact on their libido.

Clearly such side-effects ought to be considered carefully in the contraceptive decision-making process. Male condoms can impact on a man's erectile function. All these issues can often be tackled in a psycho-sexual clinic.

It is important to note that many life issues will interact with contraception. For example, in making your decisions you need to consider: your age, your health, your previous contraceptive history, whether you have had children and whether you intend to have children.

Contraception can often impact on each of the three elements mentioned at the beginning of the book – the physical, the psychological, and the relational. So a couple needs to explore this issue fully and regularly.

SEXUAL HEALTH: WHAT TO DO AND WHERE TO GO

If you have a physical symptom, such as erectile difficulty or anorgasmia, it is important to go to your GP first. You need to specify your problem to the doctor and remember that not all GPs are experts about sexual problems. The GP will attempt to eliminate medical issues, such as circulatory, hormonal and other physical conditions first.

A sexual clinic in a general hospital will serve several GP practices in a wide area. Over 75% of the patients come from 10% of the GPs. Therefore, some GPs may need persuading to refer you.

I deal with an enormous range of issues as part of my work in the hospital clinic. One common misconception is that psycho-sexual therapy is a limited discipline, but it covers psychological, physical and relational fields. The clinic may refer clients to another consultant. For example, dermatological problems are fairly common and may require specialist advice or treatment.

Often a patient will need medical advice from one specialist, and psycho-sexual help from another. The team approach to psycho-sexual problems has many layers. Interestingly, some people pick up the word 'psycho' from psycho-sexual and assume all sorts of things. Psycho is this context refers to the mental aspect of sex, and sexual to the physical.

Check things out. Ask questions of doctors and specialists about their level of knowledge and their qualifications and experience. Confidence in your therapist is essential.

Some people worry about cost but it costs no more to use a psycho-sexual therapist privately than to hire a plumber. This can be money well invested. If you think psycho-sexual therapy is expensive, try divorce!!

Pyscho-sexual clinics are good places to go and explore problems and find strategies to meet them. The therapists look at the bigger picture. If you think the problem is relational, choose a therapist who is well-versed in sexual and relational issues.

DISEASE AND SEX
To help you navigate this broad and complex subject, I have organised it into three areas:
1. Sexually transmitted diseases (STDs) – i.e. diseases transmitted by intimate contact or exchange of bodily fluids.
2. Sexual diseases – i.e. Non-sexually transmitted diseases of the genitalia, reproductive, and secondary sexual organs (such as breasts).
3. Diseases or illnesses that have an impact on sexual function.

1. STDS

STDs are rising rapidly so it is more important than ever to have good information on what may be contracted and how. Virtually all sexually transmitted diseases can be effectively treated given early diagnosis. It is completely mistaken to assume that you will show some symptoms if you have contracted an STD. For example, Chlamydia often shows no symptoms, and yet if left for months to years can cause infertility in women. A visit to a sexual health clinic or GP for simple tests – blood tests and smears – is all it takes to avoid such devastating consequences.

Bacterial vaginosis

Bacterial Vaginosis (BV) is a condition in women where the normal balance of bacteria in the vagina is disrupted and replaced by an overgrowth of certain bacteria. It is sometimes accompanied by discharge, odour, pain, itching, or burning.

How BV is contracted

● Having a new sex partner or multiple sex partners
● Douching
● Using an intra-uterine device (IUD) for contraception.

Symptoms

Women with BV may have an abnormal vaginal discharge with an unpleasant smell. Discharge is usually white or grey. Women with BV may also have burning during urination or itching around the outside of the vagina, or both. Some women with BV report no signs or symptoms at all.

Some complications

BV is associated with an increase in the development of Pelvic Inflammatory Disease (See below for PID).
● Having BV while pregnant may put a woman at increased risk for some complications of pregnancy.
● BV can increase a woman's susceptibility to other STDs, such as Chlamydia and gonorrhea.

Diagnosis and treatment
Diagnosis involves a simple test on the vaginal fluid and treatment is a course of anti-biotics.

Prevention
Do not douche
Always complete courses of treatment

Candida
(see Thrush)

Chlamydia
Description
Chlamydia is caused by the bacterium, *Chlamydia trachomatis*, which can damage a woman's reproductive organs. Even though symptoms of chlamydia are usually mild or absent, serious complications that cause irreversible damage, including infertility, can occur "silently" before a woman ever recognises a problem. Chlamydia also can cause discharge from the penis of an infected man.

In the UK it is estimated that between 1% and 2% of 16-19 year olds have the infection and it is increasing rapidly. It is the most frequently reported bacterial sexually transmitted disease in the US. An estimated 2.8 million Americans are infected with chlamydia each year. Women are frequently re-infected if their sex partners are not treated.

Chlamydia can be transmitted during vaginal, anal, or oral sex. Chlamydia can also be passed from an infected mother to her baby during childbirth.

Any sexually active person can be infected with chlamydia. The greater the number of sexual partners, the greater the risk of infection. Because the cervix (opening to the uterus) of teenage girls and young women is not fully matured, they are at particularly high risk for infection if sexually active.

Symptoms

Chlamydia is known as a 'silent' disease because about threequarters of infected women and about half of infected men have no symptoms. If symptoms do occur, they usually appear within 1 to 3 weeks after exposure.

Complications

If untreated, infections can progress to serious reproductive and other health problems with both short-term and long-term consequences. Like the disease itself, the damage that Chlamydia causes is often 'silent'. It may cause complications during pregnancy and to the unborn child; and to fertility (as mentioned above).

Diagnosis and treatment

Often a urine test or a swab. Treatment is a simple course of antibiotics.

Prevention

Condoms reduce the risk of transmission.

Genital herpes

Description

When signs do occur, they typically appear as one or more blisters on or around the genitals or rectum. The blisters break, leaving tender ulcers (sores) that may take two to four weeks to heal the first time they occur. Typically, another outbreak can appear weeks or months after the first, but it almost always is less severe and shorter than the first outbreak. Although the infection can stay in the body indefinitely, the number of outbreaks tends to decrease over a period of years. It may infect as many as a quarter of the population.

It is caused by the herpes simplex viruses type 1 (HSV-1) and type 2 (HSV-2). Most genital herpes is caused by HSV-2. Most individuals show no signs, or only minimal ones, or symptoms from HSV-1 or HSV-2 infection.

Symptoms
Most people infected with HSV-2 are not aware of their infection. However, if signs and symptoms occur during the first outbreak, they can be quite pronounced. The first outbreak usually occurs within two weeks after the virus is transmitted, and the sores typically heal within two to four weeks. Other signs and symptoms during the primary episode may include a second crop of sores, and flu-like symptoms, including fever and swollen glands. However, most individuals with HSV-2 infection may never have sores, or they may have very mild signs that they do not even notice or that they mistake for insect bites or another skin condition.

Most people diagnosed with a first episode of genital herpes can expect to have several (typically four or five) outbreaks (symptomatic recurrences) within a year. Over time these recurrences usually decrease in frequency.

Complications
These can be severe if contracted in pregnancy.

Diagnosis
Can involve a blood test or a sample of the sore.

Treatment
There is no cure, but anti-viral medications can reduce symptoms.

Prevention
Long-term monogamous relationships or the use of condoms. People with herpes should not engage in unprotected sex while sores are evident.

Genital warts
Description
Genital warts – *Human papillomavirus* (HPV infection) – are a skin condition caused by some types of HPV. They appear as growths or bumps, which may be raised or flat, single or multiple, small or large. They tend to be flesh coloured or

whitish. They usually occur in males on the penis, scrotum, anus, or groin area; in women in or around the vagina, the anus or groin.

Transmission
Through sexual and oral contact.

Diagnosis
Usually involves medical examination.

Treatment
They cannot be cured and treatments are various, ranging from creams to cryotherapy (freezing).

Prevention
Using condoms can reduce risk.

Gonorrhoea
Description
Gonorrhea is caused by *Neisseria gonorrhoeae*, a bacterium that can grow and multiply easily in the warm, moist areas of the reproductive tract, including the cervix, uterus, and fallopian tubes in women, and in the urethra (urine canal) in women and men. The bacterium can also grow in the mouth, throat, eyes, and anus. Unfortunately infection rates are on the increase in the UK.

Contraction
Gonorrhea is spread through contact with the penis, vagina, mouth, or anus. Ejaculation does not have to occur for gonorrhea to be transmitted or acquired. Gonorrhea can also be spread from mother to baby during delivery. People who have had gonorrhea and received treatment may get infected again if they have sexual contact with a person infected with gonorrhea.

Symptoms
May include burning sensation when urinating or a discharge for men and women. Women may also experience bleeding between periods. May be mild and go unnoticed.

Complications
Untreated gonorrhea can cause serious and permanent health problems in both women and men; it can be life-threatening and have serious consequences for the unborn child.

Diagnosis
Simple urine test (usually).

Treatment
Easy and successful, with antibiotics.

Prevention
Use condoms.

Hepatitis Viral
These are extremely complex liver diseases, with five forms: Hepatitis A, Hepatitis B, Hepatitis C, Hepatitis D, Hepatitis E.

You are advised to visit the web links for the UK and the US listed below and, if in any doubt, seek medical advice. Here are some notes:

Hepatitis A, caused by the hepatitis A virus (HAV), can affect anyone. It is mainly transmitted from person to person, although it can also be transmitted through food or drink. The incubation period is about 15-40 days, and the symptoms are generally mild. A vaccine against the virus is recommended for people travelling to countries with moderate or high levels of hepatitis A.

Hepatitis B is a serious disease which can cause lifelong infection, cirrhosis (scarring) of the liver, liver cancer, liver failure, and death. Early symptoms of the hepatitis B virus are flu-like, and infection can lead to liver disease and liver cancer. The virus circulates in the blood and body fluids of infected people, and spreads by sexual contact, other close contact and the sharing of needles and razors. Babies with infected mothers can also become infected during birth. However, a vaccination is available.

Hepatitis C, caused by the hepatitis C virus (HCV), is found in the blood of persons who have the disease. This is spread by contact with the blood of an infected person.

People infected with hepatitis C virus often show no symptoms initially, but long-term effects can include liver damage and cancer. The virus is transmitted by infected body fluids, and needle sharers are at particular risk. Babies can also be infected by their mothers during birth. No vaccine exists to prevent hepatitis C infection, but treatments are available that are effective in over 50% of cases.

Hepatitis D, caused by the hepatitis D virus (HDV), is a defective virus that needs the hepatitis B virus to exist, and is found in the blood of persons infected with the virus. It can be sexually transmitted.

Hepatitis E, caused by the hepatitis E virus (HEV), is transmitted in much the same way as hepatitis A virus, but is rare.

HIV and Aids
Description
The Human Immunodeficiency Virus (HIV) which causes AIDS is transmitted through body fluids in particular blood, semen, and vaginal secretions and breast milk. HIV is a fragile virus, which can only survive in a limited range of conditions. It can only enter the body through naturally moist places and cannot penetrate unbroken skin.

In the UK over 58,000 adults live with HIV, and more than one third are unaware that they are infected. [*See Box below]

> *** In November 2005, the National Aids Trust (NAT), published the following data:**
>
> "It is estimated that there are now 58,300 individuals currently living with HIV in the UK, over a third of whom (19,700) are unaware of their condition. HIV rates continue to climb. Newly diagnosed cases reported for 2004 stand at 7,275. There is a continuing epidemic among the homosexual community and men having sex with men, accounting for approximately 2,185, or 30%, of new diagnoses in 2004. The main increase, however, is among heterosexuals, the majority of whom probably acquired the virus in Africa, with 4,287 new diagnoses in 2004, accounting for 59% of all new diagnoses."

Contraction

Transmission of HIV takes place through:
- unprotected sexual intercourse with an infected partner (the most common);
- exchange of bodily fluid, including blood;
- sharing needles or other skin-piercing equipment;
- transmission from infected mother to child in the womb or at birth and breastfeeding.

Note: HIV is NOT transmitted by casual physical contact, coughing, sneezing and kissing, by sharing toilet and washing facilities, by using eating utensils or consuming food and beverages handled by someone who has HIV; it is not spread by mosquitoes or other insect bites.

Symptoms

HIV weakens the human body's immune system, making it difficult to fight infection. Symptoms may be slight, so it is important to take regular tests if you feel at risk and to practise safe sex. Early symptoms of AIDS include: chronic fatigue, diarrhoea, fever, mental changes such as memory loss, weight loss, persistent cough, severe recurrent skin rashes, herpes and mouth infections, and swelling of the lymph nodes.

Treatment

Research is currently under way into vaccines, and rapid progress is being made. Antiretroviral drugs are available to slow the progression, or delay the onset, of Aids for up to 25 years (and rising); at present these drugs are relatively expensive. The picture is changing rapidly.

Prevention

Ensure that there is a barrier to the virus, such as condoms, and that skin-piercing equipment is not contaminated. N.B. There are now PEPs (Post-exposure Prophylactics) available as morning-after pills for up to 72 hours after possible exposure to HIV, e.g. through rape or a split condom.

Non-specific urethritis (NSU)

Description

An inflammation of the man's urethra caused by Chlamydia or non-specific bacteria. Women have a vaginal discharge, pain when urinating and during intercourse, and bleeding during periods.

Symptoms

Pain during urinating or a white discharge and possibly some soreness of the glands or the tip of the penis.

Transmission

By sexual intercourse.

Diagnosis

Swabs and urine sample.

Treatment
Simple and effective course of antibiotics.

Prevention
Condoms.

Complications
Rare.

Pelvic inflammatory disease (PID)
Description
This is a general term that refers to infection of the uterus (womb), fallopian tubes (tubes that carry eggs from the ovaries to the uterus) and other reproductive organs. It is a common and serious complication of some sexually transmitted diseases (STDs), especially Chlamydia and gonorrhea. PID can damage the fallopian tubes and tissues in and near the uterus and ovaries. Untreated PID can lead to serious consequences including infertility, ectopic pregnancy (a pregnancy in the fallopian tube or elsewhere outside of the womb), abscess formation, and chronic pelvic pain.

Contraction
Often contracted as a result of gonorrhoea or Chlamydia.

Symptoms
These include: lower abdominal pain, painful intercourse and urination, as well as unusual vaginal discharge.

Complications
Damage to the fallopian tubes, which can result in infertility and ectopic pregnancy.

Diagnosis
Difficult and usually based on a pattern of clinical findings.

Treatment
It can be cured by antibiotics, but they are not always effective.

Prevention
Condoms.

Pubic lice
Description
Tiny parasitic insects that live in coarse body hair and look like crabs. Nits are their eggs which appear as brownish dots on the hair.

Transmission
Sexual or close physical contact.

Symptoms
Itching in the affected area.

Diagnosis
Visual examination.

Treatment
Very effective. Using special cream, lotion or shampoo.

Scabes
Description
Tiny parasitic mites smaller than a pinhead. They burrow into the skin and lay eggs.

Transmission
Sexual or close physical contact.

Symptoms
May only occur after six weeks – intense itching, a rash or tiny spots.

Diagnosis
Visual examination of the infected area.

Treatment
Special cream or lotion left on the skin for a period of time. Clothing and bedding need to be given a hot wash. Very effective.

Complications
Rare.

Syphilis
Description
Caused by the bacterium *Treponema pallidum*, syphilis has often been called "the great imitator" because so many of the signs and symptoms are indistinguishable from those of other diseases.

Contraction
Through direct contact with syphilis source, including genitals, anus and rectum.

Symptoms
Three stages
Primary: usually a single sore in the first 10-90 days after infection, lasting for 3-6 weeks. If untreated the symptoms go away, which is dangerous.
Secondary: skin rashes in one or more areas of the body; or red/brown spots on the palms of the hands or feet. Again, without treatment the symptoms will disappear and enter another latent phase.
Tertiary: syphilis may damage internal organs, including the brain, eyes, heart, liver etc. This may result in dementia and death.

Diagnosis
Sample from the sore or from a blood test.

Treatment
In the early stages a simple antibiotic. Longer treatment will be required for somebody in the secondary phase. In the third stage, further damage can be prevented but symptoms cannot be reversed.

Prevention
Condoms.

Note: Syphilis was in decline but is now increasing.

Thrush (Candida albicans)
Description
Thrush is caused by a fungus, a yeast that normally lives harmlessly on the skin or in the mouth, gut or vagina, usually without causing problems. Occasionally the yeast increases rapidly causing symptoms. This is called clinical thrush or candidiasis.

Symptoms
In women: itching or soreness of the vagina, vulva or anus; white vaginal discharge; pain during sex and urination. In men: irritation, burning or itching under the foreskin or on the tip of the penis; redness or red patches under the foreskin; a discharge under the foreskin or from the urethra; pain during urination.

Causes
Sexual contact. Antibiotics. Tight nylon or lycra clothing.

Diagnosis
Normally visual examination or swab.

Treatment
Anti-fungal pessaries or cream applied to the infected area.

Complications
Rare.

Prevention
Condoms.

Trichomoniasis
Description
Trichomoniasis is the most common curable STD among young, sexually active women in the US, where an estimated 7.4 million new cases occur each year in women and men. It is caused by the single-celled protozoan parasite, Trichomonas vaginalis. The vagina is the most common site of infection in women, and the urethra (urine canal) is the most common site of infection in men.

Contraction
The parasite is sexually transmitted through penis-to-vagina intercourse or vulva-to-vulva (the genital area outside the vagina) contact with an infected partner. Women can acquire the disease from infected men or women, but men usually contract it only from infected women.

Symptoms
Symptoms are more common in women. Female symptoms of infection include a frothy, yellow-green vaginal discharge with a strong odour. It also may cause discomfort during intercourse and urination, as well as irritation and itching of the female genital area. Some men may temporarily have an irritation inside the penis, mild discharge, or slight burning after urination or ejaculation, but otherwise have no symptoms.

Complications
May result in low weight and premature births.

Diagnosis
It is diagnosed by a physical examination and lab test.

Treatment
Simple drug metronidazole, given by mouth. Both partners need to be treated.

Prevention
Condoms.

Conclusions

Broadly speaking, most sexually transmitted diseases and infections are treated effectively with few complications if caught early enough. However, the consequences can be serious if untreated for a long period of time.

When a couple discover an STD within their relationship, it can carry stigma, embarrassment, and undermine trust. So it is important that they speak openly about their feelings, and support and encourage one another.

It is equally important that they get their facts right.

For example, BV and Thrush can occur spontaneously and are also transmitted. Therefore they do not necessarily indicate infidelity. Other diseases may have been contracted before the relationship. However, sometimes the diagnosis of a disease can give incontrovertible evidence of infidelity, and so it is important to work through the issues this raises.

In pregnancy, the complications from STDs can be particularly tragic. Therefore, screening before conception and careful sexual activity during pregnancy are of paramount importance.

Being selective about your partner not having had too many partners or a safe sex approach, and using condoms, are the best approaches to prevent STDs.

Obviously the more partners you have the more chance there is of contracting a sexual disease or infection.

2. SEXUAL DISEASES
I have included some conditions that often don't get picked up and have a negative effect. This is not a comprehensive list.

MEN
Prostate cancer
Symptoms
Difficulty in passing urine (restricted); frequency of urination, especially at night, blood in the urine or pain in passing urine. [N.B. These symptoms are similar to those for an enlarged prostate which is a benign condition but may require drug treatment or surgery].

Diagnosis
Initial stages with your GP, resulting in referral to a specialist if need be.

Treatment
Early diagnosis usually results in effective treatment.

Testicular cancer
Description
The most common cause of cancer in men aged 20 to 34. The cure rate is 80%.

Symptoms
Enlargement or hardness of the whole testicle or a lump.

Diagnosis
Self-examination followed by visit to GP.

Treatment
Early treatment usually results in successful cure.

Penile cancer

Symptoms

A red, velvety patch on the penis, a raw area that may have a smelly discharge or light growth. Swollen lymph nodes in the groin. Rare in men under 40. Very rare in circumcised men.

Diagnosis

Self-examination and then a visit to your GP who will normally arrange for a biopsy.

Treatment

Early diagnosis improves the prospects for successful treatment.

WOMEN

Cervical cancer

Women over the age of 25 will benefit from having regular smears to check the health of their cervix. However it is possible for younger women to develop cervical cancer. If a younger woman experiences dyspareunia, (i.e. pain deep in the abdomen during intercourse) she would be well advised to approach her GP to have a cervical smear to discount problems with her cervix.

Endometriosis

If you experience considerable pain, particularly around periods, you may have endometriosis (when tissue that lines the uterus is found outside the uterus adhering to various parts of the abdomen, such as the ovaries, fallopian tubes etc). You should go to your GP; diagnosis requires laparoscopy. If found, endometriosis can be treated by laser and/or drugs. It may recur several months later, but the improvement for 6-12 months can often enable a healthy sex life for that period – and it may not reoccur.

Hormonal levels and fatigue

Pregnancy has a profound impact on hormones. This often results in extreme fatigue after birth. However, if the fatigue does not improve after six months, do not simply attribute it to sleepless nights etc. Ask your GP for a hormonal profile. If your hormones are out of kilter, they can usually be treated easily.

The thyroid function can often be affected by pregnancy. The symptoms are excessive tiredness. It is well worth having your thyroid function checked especially if there are thyroid issues in the family.

Incontinence
After childbirth incontinence is a common problem. It should clear up within six months. If it does not, do something about it. Approach your GP; explore electrical stimulation for developing vaginal muscle tone which can cure the incontinence (many women report improvements in the quality of sex as a result of this treatment).

PID (Pelvic Inflammatory Disease)
This condition mentioned above can sometimes be treated effectively by a two-week anti-biotic course. However, if it does not cure the symptoms, you may find approaching your GP for a six-week course of antibiotics may resolve the problem.

Polycystic ovaries
This is a fairly common condition that can go undiagnosed. If a woman starts developing facial hair or irregular periods, she should ask her GP to check her hormonal profile. Untreated this condition can result in premature menopause. Hormonal treatment can often improve this condition fairly readily.

3. ILLNESSES AND DISEASES THAT AFFECT SEXUAL FUNCTION
Blood pressure
Men
Medication may affect erectile function. This issue can often be improved within a psycho-sexual clinic.

Women

Quality of orgasm can be affected negatively and again this situation may be helped through psycho-sexual support.

Depression and anxiety

Most anti-depressant medication has negative side-effects to varying degrees on libido, and both the quality and ability of orgasm or ejaculation. The only SSRI anti-depressant that has no listed side-effects for sexual function is mertazapine (zispin).

It is also worth mentioning that the symptoms of the illnesses of depression and anxiety often leave you feeling decidedly unsexy.

Diabetes

Men

Diabetes type 1 often has an affect on erectile function. This does not mean that the condition cannot be treated constructively within a psycho-sexual clinic to improve the situation. Type 2 diabetes may still have an impact even if well managed, and may benefit from exploration in a psycho-sexual setting.

Women

The affects of diabetes and sexual function on women are often neglected. It may impact negatively on libido and/or quality of orgasm. Don't settle for being told the diabetes is well managed so it will not affect sexual function. This is simply untrue. Approach your GP or diabetes centre to get a psycho-sexual referral. Merely having your experience validated in a psycho-sexual setting can start to improve your sex life.

Heart Disease

Men and Women

Coronary disease sufferers are often scared to have sex. While this is understandable, this fear can be tackled within the psycho-sexual setting. In short, a treadmill test can often indicate definitively whether sexual exertion and excitement are safe.

CHAPTER 14

Resources and contacts

UK
Intelligent Sex
www.intelligentsex.co.uk

Department of Health
The mission of the DhS is to "modernise sexual services, halt the spread of sexually transmitted infections and reduce the numbers of unintended pregnancies".
http://www.dh.gov.uk/PolicyAndGuidance/HealthAndSocialCareTopics/
SexualHealth/fs/en

NHS Direct
Free helpline offering information on all health issues. Tel: 0845 4647
Website: www.nhsdirect.nhs.uk

Herpes Virus Association (HVA)
www.hva.org.uk
Tel: 020 7607 9661

HIV/AIDS
THT (Terrence Higgins Trust)
Tel: 0845 122 1200
Web: www.tht.org.uk

African AIDS helpline
Tel: 0800 0967 500

Positively Women
Helpline answered by HIV positive women
Tel: 020 7713 0222
Web: www.positivelywomen.org.uk

Sexual Health Direct (run by the Family Planning Association)
Tel: 0800 567 123
Tel: 0845 3101334
Web: www.playingsafely.co.uk

Society of Sexual Health
Web: www.ssha.info

US
The Centers for Disease Control and Prevention (CDC) is one of the 13 major operating components of the US government's Department of Health and Human Services (HHS).
Web: http://www.cdc.gov/std/

COUNSELLING ORGANISATIONS
Asian Family Support
Send a SAE for lists of local therapists. Confidential marital and personal counselling service. PO Box 13686, London SW20 9ZH
Tel: 020 8539 5566

British Association of Sexual and Relational Therapy (BASRT) for a list of clinics and psycho-sexual therapists on their website. In the Health Service you will find competent and qualified psycho-sexual advisers.
Tel/fax: 020 8543 2707
e-mail: info@basrt.org.uk
web: www.basrt.org.uk

British Association for Counselling and Psychotherapy (BACP)
Aiming to make counselling and psychotherapy widely recognised as a profession whose purpose and activity is understood by the general public.
BACP House, 35-37 Albert Street, Rugby, Warwickshire CV21 2SG
Tel: 0870 443 5252
Web: www.bacp.co.uk

Counsellors in Primary Care

An organisation which represents counsellors and psychotherapists working in primary care and which aims to establish national standards and guidelines for further development of counselling throughout the NHS. CPC is a self-regulating membership association; the names of individual members who reach the required standards for membership criteria are entered on a Register of Members.

Web: http://www.cpc-online.co.uk/

Relate

Counselling service for adults with relationship problems. Your nearest branch will be listed in the phone book.

Herbert Gray College, Little Church Street, Rugby, Warwickshire CV21 3AP

Tel: 0845 456 1310

Web: http://www.relate.org.uk

uktherapists.com

Provides directories for finding psychotherapists, counsellors, and complementary practitioners. Also offers a variety of therapy services for public and professionals alike.

Web: www.uktherapists.com

Youth Access

Phone for details of a young person's counselling service near you.

1a Taylors Yard, 67 Alderbrook Road, London SW1Z 8AD

Tel: 020 8772 9900

SEXUAL HEALTH
British Society for Sexual Medicine (BSSM)
www.bssm.org.uk

European Sexual Dysfunction Alliance (ESDA)
www.esda.eu.com

European Society for Sexual and Impotence Research (ESSIR)
www.essir.net

Institute of Psychosexual Medicine
www.ipm.org.uk

International Society for Impotence Research (ISIR)
www.urolog.nl/artsen/isir/

International Society for the Study of the Aging Male (ISSAM)
www.issam.ch

Journal of Sexual and Relationship Therapy
www.tandf.co.uk/journals/titles/14681994.html

European Federation of Sexology
www.europeansexology.com

Men's Health Matters
Advice and support by trained nurses in a range of medical issues affecting men.
Blythe Hall, 100 Blythe Road, London, W14 0HB
Tel: 020 8995 4448

Malehealth.co.uk
Site run by the Men's Health Forum, the UK's leading charity working to improve men's health. Provides accurate, easy-to-use information about the key health problems that affect men.
Tavistock House, Tavistock Square, London WC1H 9HR
Website: www.malehealth.co.uk

National Library of Medicine (NLM) and National Institute of Health (US)
This site is a directory of compilations of links on topics relating to men's health. Topics addressed include prostate cancer, erectile dysfunction, infertility, vasectomy, male menopause, and male breast cancer. Selected topics address issues related to boys and women.
Website: www.nlm.nih.gov/medlineplus/menshealth.html

Sexual Dysfunction Association
Charitable organisation was set up to help sufferers of impotence (erectile dysfunction) and their partners and to raise awareness of the condition.
Windmill Place Business Centre, 2-4 Windmill Lane, Southall, Middlesex UB2 4NJ
Helpline: 0870 774 3571
Website: www.sda.uk.net/index1.htm

Sex Education Forum
Sex education materials and information for children and young people.
8 Wakeley Street, London, EC1V 7QE
Tel: 020 7843 6056
Website: www.ncb.org.uk/sef/

Terrence Higgins Trust
Practical support, help, counselling and advice for anyone with, or concerned about, AIDS and HIV infection.
52–54 Grays Inn Road, London WC1X
Website: www.tht.org.uk

Women's Health Concern

Specialises in helping women with gynaecological and hormonal conditions and advises on the proper use of HRT.

PO Box 2126, Marlow, Bucks SL7 2RY

Tel: 01628 483612

Website: www.womens-health-concern.org

Women's Health

Helps women make informed information about their health, publishes a range of factsheets.

52 Featherstone Street, London, EC1 8RT

Tel: 020 7251 6333

Helpline: 0845 125 5254

Website: www.womenshealthlondon.org.uk

YOUNG PEOPLE

Brook Young People's Information Service

Free confidential helpline and online inquiry service for people under 25.

0800 0185 023

www.brook.org.uk

Sexwise

Free confidential helpline for people under 18 on all sex and relationship issues.

0800 28 29 30

www.ruthinking.co.uk

OTHER

BBC

Relationships and sexual health

http://www.bbc.co.uk/relationships/

MARIE STOPES ONE CALL
Sexual health information and services for women and men.
Marie Stopes House, 153-157 Cleveland Street, London W1T 6QW
Tel: 0845 300 8090
Website: www.mariestopes.org.uk

NATIONAL AIDS HELPLINE
Free 24-hour confidential advice on all aspects of HIV/Aids.
Tel: 0800 567123
Website: www.nat.org.uk

NATIONAL FRIEND
UK network of lesbian, gay and bisexual helplines. Support and advice by phone
or letter on all matters including sexual help.
216 The Custard Factory, Gibb Street, Digbeth, Birmingham B9 4AA
Tel: 0121 684 1261
Website: www.friend.dircon.co.uk

RUTHINKING.CO.UK
Free helpline giving the chance to talk to an adviser about sex and personal
relationships.
Tel: 0800 282930
Website: www.ruthinking.co.uk

GENDER ISSUES
The Beaumont Society
Offers advices and support to transgendered people and their partners.
27 Old Gloucester Street, London WC1N 3XX
Tel: 01582 412220
Website: www.beaumontsociety.org.uk

Gender Dysphoria Trust
Advice and information on gender and sexual orientation.
PO Box 3192, Brighton BN1 3WR
Tel: 01273 234024
Helpline: 07000 790347
Website: www.gendertrust.org.uk

CONTRACEPTION AND PREGNANCY
Brook Advisory Service
Clinics for young people for advice on contraception, abortion, sexual and relationship problems.
Unit 421 Highgate Studios, 52-79 Highgate Road, London NW5 1TL
Tel: 0800 018 5023
Website: www.brook.org.uk/content/

Family Planning Service (Formerly the Family Planning Association)
Tel: 020 7923 5228
Email: library&information@fpa.org.uk
Website: www.fpa.org.uk

FP Sales
Website: www.fpsales.co.uk

Further Reading
Becoming Orgasmic, by Julia R Herman and Joseph LoPiccolo (Piatkus, 1999)
Human Sexuality and it's problems, by John Bancroft (Churchill Livingstone, 1989)
Sex Therapy, by Keith Hawton (Oxford Medical Publishers, 1993)

INDEX